ODYSSEUS
the WANDERER

ODYSSEUS
the WANDERER

by

AUBREY DE SÉLINCOURT

Illustrated by

NORMAN MEREDITH

CRITERION BOOKS, NEW YORK, N. Y.

Contents

ODYSSEUS
the WANDERER

{ Ithaca }

So, TRAVELER, YOU want a story. They say that here in Greece there's a story under every stone—and that's a lot, if you take a look at these hills I scratch and sow my handful of grain on for a living. But I'm a poor hand at story-telling. If it had been my father, now . . . he was a great one for stories. You couldn't stop him—and didn't want to. When I was a boy, and that wasn't yesterday, mind you, he told me about Odysseus. . . .

3

So you've heard of Odysseus, stranger? Ah, but you don't know what my father knew about him. Odysseus was a native of these parts, and that makes all the difference.

Now eat your supper and drink what's in your cup, and I'll try to tell you the tale again, remembering my father's words; and when I forget them you must forgive me. My tongue runs on fast enough; but that's not the same as telling a story.

It will do me good to tell it you. How can a man live dumb as an ox, year in year out, with never a friend to wag his chin at? Few travelers pass this way across the mountains. They like the railroad best, and the big ports full of steamships from I don't know where. I've never seen the railroad—would you believe it?—living all my life on these poor acres of mine by the sea, and never going beyond the village behind the hill over there, where the church is. But I've seen the steamships—look, there's one there now, going to the northward with her own smoke following her like a cloud. How she eats up the miles of sea, fair weather or foul, with no need to wait for a slant of wind like the coasting schooners or the little caïques—which put me in mind of the old ships my father spoke of.

Now what I'm going to tell you happened a while since; how long, the likes of me have no means of knowing—but before my father was born, or my grandfather, or *his* father either; a great while ago, in better days than these, when a man if he had little to content him at home could take a ship and look elsewhere. Perhaps he was killed in battle, or knocked on the head by robbers, or drowned; but if his luck was in, he found what he wanted—and not only money and cattle either. There was life for a man then, when there was little law but fate, and God's will, and his own shame.

Fill up again, my friend, and let's drink together. Look, I turn down my cup and pour these drops on the ground.

Poseidon, brother of Zeus, lord of the sea, girdler of the world. . . .

There's no need to start like that, my

friend, or look behind you. Did you think there was a priest over there, hiding in the olives? Don't be afraid; I only whispered, and now—see—I cross myself, and all is well again.

How calm the sea is! Its voice in the bay is like a sigh. The death which comes out of the sea is the gentlest of all: a moment of fear, a little pain, then falling asleep. It is hard to live by the sea, as I do, and be too poor to build a boat and follow the sun out there behind the islands.

Forgive my tongue for wandering. When a man lives alone with only his pigs and two oxen for company the words crowd so thick in his throat that he must let them out, or they'll choke him. God sends guests; evening is the time for tales. Come then, and I'll begin.

You see that dark hump far out on the sea, under the sun? Not the big island there, but a little to the northward: a hump like a whale's back dark on the water. Tomorrow at sunrise it will glow as pink as a rose, and before noon it will shine white like snow. But dark or bright the seamen see it, even across thirty

miles of sea. That's Ithaca: rocky Ithaca.
Grapes grow on it, and olives and figs; but
there are no cornlands or pasture for horses;
only a few goats on the craggy hills. It's so
small that even inland a man feels himself still
in the midst of the sea, the sound of it in his
ears, the dazzle in his eyes, the smell in his
nostrils, and the glory of it in his heart.

There in Ithaca, Odysseus was born. What's
in a name? Odysseus . . . *the man the Gods
were angry with*. Think as you please, stranger;
man is born to sorrow, friends deceive, life is
short, the dark waits for all; yet Odysseus,
whether the Gods were angry or not, took life
into his hands like a ripe fig and sucked the
sweetness out to the last drop. What if he did
lose his way in the pathless sea, looking for
the Great Brown Mountain at the end of the
world? No doubt in some foreign land he
sighed now and then for the smoke going up
from the roofs of Ithaca, and for the sound
of the stream splashing into the bowl of rock
by the steep track; yet if anyone said to him,
"What have you done, Odysseus, that the Gods

are angry?" he would be silent, and glancing
at his questioner with a flicker of malice in his
old eyes, stare out again over the sea. For he
knew that it was only half the truth that troubles come from heaven; the other half was
that a man brings them on himself by his own
desires—and often trouble itself is its own best
reward. What else are a man's wits for, his
cunning and skill and strength, if not to be
used to kill an enemy, or save a friend, or win
fame?

For some men home is a place to start from,
not to live in. Such a man was Odysseus. Yet
he loved Ithaca. There was no wine for him
like the wine from his father Laertes' grapes,
no figs so black and sweet as the figs that grew
by the wall of his father's house on the hill.
He carried the thought of them to the ends
of the earth, a childhood memory, an old
man's dream. It was well for him he did; for
without that love his voyages would have been
like the whirling of atoms spinning perpetually through the void, yet never reaching another place.

Even as a child he was seldom in his father's house. Having no brothers or sisters, he cared little for children's play, but was off as soon as his legs would carry him to the meeting place of men, or to the seashore, where he would practice with weapons of hunting or war, the spear, the knife, and the bow made by his father to fit his small strength. As time went on he would be away most days at the shipyard in the town, watching the riggers and shipbuilders at work, asking them questions about their craft and lending a hand when they would let him. They took to the boy readily enough, seeing he was quick and clever, and let him into not a few of their mysteries, teaching him to drill holes in the plank with an iron drill, spinning it cunningly with the leather thong, and to drive in the wooden pins good and true. Moreover, as Laertes his father was the man of chief consequence in the island, they were eager to stand well with the son.

There too, while the boy worked or watched by the launching slips, he would listen to the

yarns of foreign captains who had brought
vessels to the island for trade or watering, and
sometimes hear with a pang of mingled excitement and pity a tale of men driven from their
homes by marauders, or by tribes on the move
from the northward, who had killed their
women, caught what men they could for
slaves, and taken their cattle and lands.

At other times he would go to the little
haven at the southern point of the island,
where the stream was that tumbled into the
stone basin, and brimmed it over, and trickled
away into the rocks and sand. It was lonely
there between the two promontories of rock,
and the sleepy sound of the stream mingling
with the lapping of the sea deepened the
quietness, except when women from the great
house came down to wash the linen, trampling
it with their feet in the clear water, and laughing and jabbering as hard as they could.

But the boy liked it best when it was lonely.
He could dream then, and watch the cloud
shadows cross the neighboring islands, Ceph-
allenia and wooded Zante and Dulichium,

or look westward towards Sicily whence his
friends the seamen brought stories of savage
men, and whirlpools, and dangerous tide rips,
and sudden squalls off the land.

One day soon, when he was old enough, he
would go to sea himself and find out if the
stories were true. He would build a fine black
ship with vermilion bows and a great painted
eye on either side, to help her to find her way
on a moonlit night, and sail to Sicily and beyond, as far as the place where the sun sank in
the sea; and southward round the stormy
Cape Malea to those eastern lands which were
ringing with the fame of the young Agamemnon. Already they called him King of Men,
because he was rich and powerful and had a
house like a castle on the mountains at Mycenæ, where the hill tracks ran from the
southern to the northern sea. Agamemnon
was a greater man even than Laertes, and
could command an army bigger by hundreds
if need be. Moreover, there was going to be a
war. Mutterings and rumors of it were in all
men's mouths. Ever since he could remember,

stories had been coming in of the growing power of a city called Troy, far away to the eastward beyond the Ægean sea: Troy, the most hated of cities—the robber city, blocking the trade route to the east and forcing tribute from the merchants and seamen of Greece and the islands. Troy must be pulled down, blotted out, burned by fire; sooner or later the ships of Greece must be assembled and the war begin, and he, Odysseus, would play his part in it, with his own black ship, and his spear, and his bow.

I could tell you much about the boyhood of this man: how as he grew stronger and taller he made himself the master of the other boys in Ithaca, loved by a few, envied by many; and how he beat them at their sports when they could get him to compete, in running and wrestling and shooting with the bow. With the bow he was a wonder. He would take a broad axe with a double head and stick it in the ground, and shoot his arrow between the blades to the mark beyond: then between two —or four—or six. When others tried the feat,

Liodes perhaps, or Antinoüs or Eurynomus, boys like himself and sons of chiefs, their arrows went wide, or struck the iron blade and were shivered to splinters; then Odysseus would laugh, and they would go away angry, grumbling that Odysseus had set the axes askew and cheated them. And so he had, for all I know.

But I have better things to tell than boys' tricks or boys' dreaming.

It is hard, having a listener, not to stretch out my story just for the pleasure of it; but if I did, before I came to the end the stars would have grown faint in tomorrow's dawn, Arcturus and Boötes and the Great Bear which alone never sets in the sea.

Now in the course of time, when Odysseus was already a young man, news came to Ithaca that men of note from all parts of Greece, good fighting men and rich chieftains, were gathering in Sparta at the house of Tyndareus, who ruled that country, to make their bids for the hand of his daughter Helen. When Odysseus heard of this, he turned the matter over in his mind, sitting on a rock in the little harbor where the stream was. Then he went up the steep track toward his house. On the way he met Melanthius his father's goatherd, a crooked, swarthy man with shifty eyes and a tuft on his chin like one of his own goats, which wagged as he talked.

Odysseus said to him: "If you were a prince like me, old goat-face, would you put in your bid for Helen's hand?"

"She has the face of a dog," Melanthius answered, and spat on the ground.

Odysseus laughed, and presently, as he passed through the farm which lay between the house and the sea, he saw Eumæus, his father's swineherd, driving the pigs from their sties.

"Eumæus," he said, "shall I go to Sparta to ask for Helen, who old goat-beard says has the face of a dog?"

"Master," Eumæus answered, "Helen is beautiful; but beauty and death walk hand in hand."

In the great hall of the house the woman

Eurycleia, who had nursed Odysseus when he
was a baby, was setting the maidservants about
their work.

"Nurse," Odysseus said, "is it true that
beauty and death go hand in hand?"

"Beauty is as beauty does, my dear," the
nurse answered. "We're all owed to death.
Only God has physic for all ills, and there's a
scorpion under every stone—so mind he
doesn't bite you. But what is it, my dear, that's
in your heart this fine morning? You were always a deep one."

Odysseus said nothing, but passed on to an
inner room to find his mother. The nurse
watched him with the anxiety of love as he
opened the door and shut it behind him.

"Mother," Odysseus said, "I am going to
Sparta to try my luck with Helen. Wish me
Godspeed."

Now Anticleia was proud of her son, and
thought no woman could have one braver or
handsomer or cleverer. Young as he was, he
had already proved his manhood and sagacity,
and knowledge of the ways and weaknesses of

men, going on missions to right his father's wrongs, and always knowing when words were better than deeds to gain an end. And of all men in Ithaca and the islands there was none who could handle a ship like him or nurse her more delicately in a hard wind and a following sea. Yet for all this his mother knew he was reckless and wild, and thirsty for adventure and fame.

"I wish you Godspeed," she said. "Mothers must endure—and hope. Helen is an evil name. Helen—the Destroyer."

Then Odysseus found his father Laertes in the herb garden which he loved, and said: "Father, fit me out a ship, a good one, with all new gear and vermilion bows, and let me choose a crew to man her, for I'm going to the court of Tyndareus to bring back Helen as my wife."

"What will you offer for her?" said Laertes. "I am not so rich, remember, as envious people suppose."

"Nothing, Father."

"Nothing?"

Odysseus laughed again. "If she wants me she can take me," he said. "There are more fish in the sea than one. If the mullet escapes, I'll catch a tunny. I'll never break my heart for a woman—or my father's fortune either."

Laertes promised the ship, and gave his son his blessing, greatly approving his sound sense. But he couldn't help giving him a word of advice, all the same.

"Remember," he said, "that God lightly steals a man's wits. Helen is beautiful. Remember, too, that it's friends who betray—we can all avoid enemies as a seaman avoids rocks."

Soon the day for sailing came. Odysseus said his farewells, first to Laertes and Anticleia, then to Eumæus, who though a servant was yet his friend, and lastly to his old nurse. She, poor woman, was more loth to let him go even than his mother was, for she still loved him as her baby, and had not the mother's pride in a son's fame.

"What call have you to get a wife," she said dabbing her eyes to dry the tears, "and you

hardly a man yet? I nursed you in my arms, I did, and when the boar gashed your thigh, it was I who brought you back to strength when you came home. And now you'll leave us again and never come back—that you won't. The world is full of danger and mischief, what with the witches and bad men and monsters and ghosts and everything dreadful—and this Helen—who knows she isn't double-faced, and

as bad as a thorn with no rose? You are brave
and clever, my darling, and as beautiful as a
palm tree, yes, you are, and a great talker, as
I am, but with more sense, for you know when
to talk and when to be silent. Silence has its
reward, and there's no danger in it. Ah, but
you'll make yourself rich and famous, that
you will—gold's the best of hosts—and come
home a married man, for not Helen or any
woman could say no to one like you, and then
you'll be looking at her all day long, with
never a word to throw at your old nurse. But
sure I'll do my duty, as a woman must—"

With that, the nurse gave a great sniff and
seized Odysseus' hand and kissed it, and a moment afterwards Odysseus was gone.

He went down to the sea and to his ship,
and found his crew already aboard. She was a
good ship, Ithaca's best: long and with a fine
run aft for speed and safety in a seaway;
painted black, with the three top strakes in
her bows scarlet for a third of their length; her
stern rising in a curve like a swan's neck above
the gunwale. She had a single mast, short and

stout, stepped well inboard, with a great yard crossing it, and stayed with ropes of twisted hide, springier and stronger than hemp. Her gunwales were pierced for oars, ten a side, and she was open for all her length except for a short space forward of the mast.

Slowly they pulled her from the quay, and, when they had an offing, the oars were unshipped and the big flaxen square sail set. Sheets and braces were brought aft and secured, a shudder came over the surface of the sea under a puff of wind from the north, the gear creaked as the sail filled and it took the strain, and the wave of her wake followed the ship as she ran to the southward.

{ What Happened in Sparta }

WHEN ODYSSEUS CAME to the house of Tyndareus in Sparta, he hadn't been there ten minutes before he felt a foot taller and twice the man he'd been at home. It was not, to be sure, the first time he had traveled: there had been that visit, for instance, to his grandfather, when he had gone hunting on the foothills of Parnassus and the boar had gashed him above the knee, and Iphitus, his father's friend, had given him his bow—a fearsome weapon which ordinary men couldn't even

21

string, let alone draw; and there had been the affair in Messenia when he had negotiated so skilfully on Laertes' behalf about compensation for a cattle raid in Ithaca. But neither his grandfather's house nor anything he had seen in Messenia was to be compared for grandeur with the house of Tyndareus. It wasn't a house; it was a palace. It was full of people and humming with life. Each man one met was richer and more famous than the last—if one could take his word for it. There was talk all day long and half the night, and a tremendous lot of eating and drinking at the long tables in the hall; and not ordinary drinking either, but all out of huge golden cups embossed with figures; gallons of strong wine, sweet as honey, dipped from silver bowls as big as a horse trough. The tables creaked under the weight of roast meat and crisp loaves in baskets. There were storytellers too—professional men—to enliven the dinners; and they spoke and sang with such a power of enchantment that one hardly knew if their tales were lies or truth, and certainly didn't care.

Many a famous man who before was only a
name to Odysseus—Diomed and Amphima-
chus, Menelaus and Philoctetes, Agapenor,
Podalirius, Patroclus—now stood before him
in flesh and blood. And Tyndareus himself
did the honors of his house like the prince he
was.

No wonder the young Odysseus trod on air.

For weeks the wooing of Helen went merrily on. It was the grandest auction you've ever
seen. Some of the young men offered more
than half their fortune for her, and nearly
came to blows when they were outbid by the
next. Sometimes at supper, before the stories,
Tyndareus would send for the girl and she
would come down from her room into the hall,
with two serving-women, and stand for a minute by a pillar near her father's chair, with a
veil over her face. All those young men would
look at her once, and then look away, and
there would be silence, as if a spirit had troubled them. Then Tyndareus, when she was
gone, would call on this man or that by name
and ask him to make his offer. Now there was

a certain Ajax amongst them, known to be the strongest man in Greece, and the stupidest. When he moved, you could see the muscles swell and breathe under his skin, crawling about like live creatures; but he was weak in the head and a great boaster.

When Tyndareus asked him what gift he would give for his daughter, he promised a thousand oxen, two thousand sheep, and vessels of gold and bales of linen more than a man can count or remember.

"What? Have you so much?" said Tyndareus.

"No," said Ajax.

"Then how can you offer it?"

Ajax growled that he would soon get it, and more. It was all one to a man like him where the cattle were; there were plenty over the border, weren't there? and he'd rustle them up any day between dinner and sundown—and bad luck to the owners of them.

The young men tittered at this, except those whose lands lay near the lands of Ajax, and Odysseus gravely said that any father should be proud of so generous a son-in-law. Ajax smiled — then frowned — then glared — then glanced at his huge fist, which happened to be lying on the table like something which belonged to him.

"And you, Odysseus, son of Laertes," said Tyndareus, "what gifts do you offer for my daughter's hand?"

"None."

There was silence at this; then a murmur amongst the guests, spreading along the polished benches and filling the hall.

"He offers nothing," said Ajax. "He means to mock us."

The murmuring grew louder, and there might have been a sad end to that day's drinking if Odysseus had not turned their thoughts to something else.

"I offer myself," he cried above the noise of voices; "may the best man win her—or the best ox."

As he said this he looked at Ajax, and in a moment the angry murmurs changed to laughter, for it was an open secret that Ajax was known as the beef-witted lord.

For days afterwards things were not comfortable in the house of Tyndareus. Indeed, they seldom were when Odysseus was anywhere about; for he was a great stirrer-up of trouble, and liked things hot and lively. Ajax was in a rage, and would gladly have cut Odysseus' throat if he had not feared it might spoil his chance for Helen. Some took his part, and some Odysseus'; and though in Tyndareus' house, and at the games which he organized from time to time to amuse his guests, it was necessary to preserve a certain seemliness, there was, nevertheless, a growing unease, born of rancor and suspicion.

Tyndareus himself was not happy. It is a fine thing for a father to have a prince to woo his daughter, or even two princes, or perhaps three. But when there are fifty of them, all high-spirited and quarrelsome, it is apt to be awkward. It was not, moreover, only Ajax and Odysseus who were the cause of the trouble: more and more Tyndareus began to fear that whoever it was that turned out to be the lucky man, he would arouse such envy in the unsuccessful that there was bound to be blood-letting. He wished Helen was safely off his hands —or not more beautiful than other men's daughters.

Odysseus, of course, was well aware of the way things were shaping: indeed, he continued to do his best to fan the flames—not only, moreover, because he enjoyed doing so, but for another reason. He had a purpose.

Now whatever his intention may have been when he sailed from Ithaca, by the time he had been a week in Sparta he had not the least desire to marry Helen. Helen was beautiful—but she wasn't the wife for him. Not by a long way. At his first sight of her his heart had grown faint within him and his knees turned to water, like everyone else's. At her second appearance, he had not looked at all, for precautionary reasons. For Odysseus had sense—and Helen wouldn't do. Moreover, there was Penelope, Icarius' daughter, whom he had met, as luck would have it, on his journey to Sparta.

Penelope was beautiful too, but only as other women are beautiful, with a sweet and comfortable beauty. She could cook and keep house and weave linen, and could be trusted to love and obey her husband, when she had one, and ask no questions. No sensible man could wish for more.

But how to win her? That was the point.

It seemed that the most likely way was to enlist the support of Tyndareus—for Tyndareus was a great prince, and Icarius would listen to him. Clearly there was no hope of winning Tyndareus' support merely by offering nothing for his daughter Helen; that was likely to have an opposite effect. So Odysseus hit upon another plan. He would stir up as much trouble as he could amongst Helen's suitors, until the threat of open violence in his house became unbearable for Tyndareus, and then suggest to him a plan for pacifying them. Tyndareus would be so grateful for the pacifying that it would never occur to him that it was Odysseus who was also the chief cause of the threat, and he would show his gratitude by asking Icarius to give Penelope to Odysseus.

It all happened just as Odysseus wished. He bided his time until the kettle of ill will amongst the rivals was just on the boil, so that Tyndareus dared not choose any one of them for fear of his murder by the rest; and then he proposed his excellent plan.

"Tyndareus," he said, "never before has a woman been the cause of such envy and contention as your daughter, Helen. Blood will be spilt in your house."

Tyndareus said that this was indeed so.

"But listen to me," Odysseus said, "and all will be well. Choose which of us you will, and bind the others by an oath to avenge him if ever Helen should bring him shame."

Tyndareus was so pleased with the plan that he at once forgot his annoyance with Odysseus for offering nothing as a bride-gift. He knew the plan was a good one, because once the oath was sworn it would certainly be kept; not even Ajax would dare to break it, the consequences would be too frightful.

That very night, therefore, at supper, before the minstrels began their storytelling, Tyndareus sent for his daughter and told her to come down into the hall. As before, there

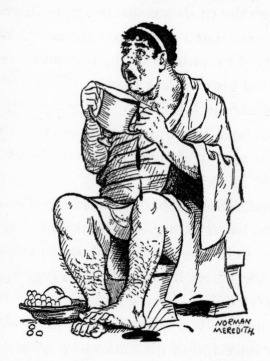

was a hush as she took her place beside the pillar near her father's chair. The young men looked at her once, then looked away, troubled: all except Ajax, who gulped his wine and stared at her as if he would eat her. For a moment Tyndareus did not speak, but let her stand by the pillar, as cool as a lily, strange as a star, and as secret as the dawn.

Then he said: "My lords and princes, flower of Greece, noblest of the Achæans, listen. To one amongst you I must give Helen my daughter. Before I name him, let all swear to avenge him, whoever he may be, if ever Helen should bring evil upon his house."

The oath was sworn, a terrible oath such as even Gods would fear to break; and so wonderful was the power of it that those angry rivals became like brothers against their will.

Then Tyndareus, relieved of his fear, gave Helen to Menelaus for his wife. And that was the end of the wooing of Helen.

It was also the beginning of the wooing of Penelope, a much easier business. Tyndareus was willing enough to put in his word on Odysseus' behalf, and in less than no time Odysseus was on his way home to Ithaca—a married man, as his old nurse had foretold in her lament, but with a different wife from the one she had expected.

[Outbreak] of War

Tyndareus was old when Helen was married to Menelaus, and like a sensible father turned over his land and power to his daughter and her husband. So Menelaus and his brother Agamemnon became lords of the twin realms of Argos and Mycenæ, and were feared by all in the southern parts of Greece.

Menelaus thought himself lucky to be called a king and to have for his wife the most beautiful woman in the world. But the Gods laughed, for they thought otherwise.

In Ithaca everyone was delighted when Odysseus came home, not with Helen, but with Penelope. The old nurse was out of her senses with joy, and called him her pet, her darling, dearest head, her little armful, and her honored master all in one breath, and took Penelope straight to her heart like a second child. Laertes did not resign his house as Tyndareus had done; nevertheless, being proud of his son, he began to give place to him at public councils in the island, taking pleasure in his gallant bearing and gay and ready speech, and himself spending more and more of his time in his beloved garden amongst the fruit trees and the vegetables.

Odysseus was happy, loving his wife and loving his home, and pleased with the new respect he had won by his recent travels, and the fact that he had been received into that grand company in Sparta. Nevertheless, there was a voice inside him, which kept whispering that he was never meant to be a family man and settle down to the management of an estate. Penelope was aware of this, but being a good wife she said little. When her son Telemachus was born, she hoped the small creature might hold him and help to settle him. But as time went on he grew more restless still and spent much time, as he used to do in his boyhood, down by the shipyard or the harbor, watching the comings and goings of ships, and listening with his old eagerness to stories of that great enemy of man, the sea. Life in Tyndareus' palace, in the great and fashionable world, had been fine while it lasted; but it was not what he wanted. What he wanted, nothing could give him but the sea.

Meanwhile the rumors of coming war against Troy had not stopped. But the prospect of it no longer fired Odysseus as it used to do long ago. War was all very well. One might grow rich on it—or one might not. But the trouble with war was, that a man was bound to a purpose not his own, and had to do what he was told. That was irksome. What had Troy to do with Ithaca, anyway? His thoughts of war had been a boy's dream; now he had better things to do: his own things, his own purposes. No need now to ask his father for a ship; he was master himself of the best in Ithaca. Suddenly—soon perhaps—the impulse would come, and he would be off.

Then one day, when Telemachus was a year old and so like his father that Odysseus laughed to look at him, a ship put in at Ithaca with news. She was a trading vessel, and her captain was an old friend of Odysseus. He found Odysseus on the beach, and almost before he was near enough to speak, his news jumped out of his mouth like a live frog, so eager he was to tell it.

"Odysseus," he cried, "it is war! A thousand ships are gathering at Aulis, and a huge army under Agamemnon, king of men. Troy will be sacked."

"Good luck to them," said Odysseus. "They'll need it; there'll be more grief than gain in such a war."

The sea captain was taken aback by this answer. But he had more to tell.

"Odysseus," he said, "they will hold you to your oath."

"What oath? I never swore to fight at Troy." The captain, who was fat, and out of breath from his hurry to find Odysseus, stood staring at him goggle-eyed with astonishment.

"But," he said, not without relish in the bringing of bad news, "haven't you heard? Are you in Ithaca so far from the world, like the black Ethiops or the ice-men of the north, that you don't know what all Greece and the eastern islands are ringing with? Helen has fled to Troy."

"Helen. . . ." The name rang like a sullen bell in Odysseus' heart. He bit his lips and looked on the ground. Suddenly he heard a cackle of laughter behind him, and a cracked voice said, "Helen! She has the face of a dog." He turned, and there was Melanthius the goatherd. Odysseus would have struck him with his fist, if he hadn't skipped nimbly away on his bandy legs up the rocky path and disappeared.

Then the captain poured out his story, and

Odysseus had to listen despite himself: how
Paris, son of Priam, the Lord of Troy, had
come to Menelaus' house, and had made
Helen love him, and had stolen her away to
Troy, and how the word had gone out through
Greece and the islands that all who swore the
oath in the house of Tyndareus should remem-
ber it now, and avenge her.

Odysseus felt his heart turn black with
anger. For once he was caught in his own trap;

for it was he who had proposed the oath, for
his own ends. He would have escaped if he
could by any stratagem; he cared not a rap for
Helen or her husband; he would have feigned
sickness, feigned madness—anything to relieve
him from the burden of useless years he too
clearly saw ahead. But nothing could be done.
The words a man speaks are not air, but living
powers; they fly lightly away and seem forgotten, but sooner or later they return to him
with their burden of destiny; and a broken
oath haunts him like a fury even beyond death.

So it was that Odysseus, against his will,
went to the war.

{ The Sack of a City }

I T IS A true saying that a man's character is his fate, and everyone knows that if he wants a thing badly enough, he'll get it in the end. There was no need for Odysseus to curse his luck for having to serve at Troy, instead of taking a ship and sailing beyond the sunset to find he knew not what; for because of that disastrous war, even he got his bellyful of voyaging: he learned more of the power and majesty and malice of the sea, and

39

brought home taller stories of monsters and
mermaids and enchanted islands than any seaman before him had thought or dreamed of.
Even the war itself had its compensations, as
wars do for some folk—the more's the pity.

Odysseus was never one for doing things by
halves; once he had made up his mind (indeed
he couldn't have done otherwise) to join the
expedition, he plunged into the business head
over ears, and drank delight of his own
strength and recklessness and cunning more
deeply than any other man in the armies of
Greece. It was not the sort of war the Greeks
had hoped for when the navy sailed from
Aulis: not such as all men fancy, or try to
fancy, at the beginning of a great campaign—
the swift blow, the sweeping victory, the glad
return. Some enterprises, it seems, have heav-
en's curse on them—or so men say, blaming
God for their own misdeeds. So it was with the
war. It was a bad war; bad in its beginning,
and bad in its end. For when the fleet was
gathered at Aulis the wind flew into the east,
and blew hard, and pinned them there; for

weeks it blew, and the fighting men rotted in
idleness and grew mutinous. Many deserted;
no captain or general, not Agamemnon himself, could exact obedience. And then it was
that a priest came to Agamemnon and whispered to him: "Give them a sign."

"What sign?"

"A sacrifice to the Gods."

"The best of my sheep?"

"No, not a sheep."

"The best of my oxen?"

"No, not an ox."

"What then?"

"The life you love best."

And Agamemnon knew that the priest
meant his daughter.

The deed was done. The girl was gagged,
and with only her eyes to plead was brought
to the stone of sacrifice. They cut her throat
and caught the blood in a bowl, and the wind
changed—fair into the west. That was the beginning; and after ten dreary years the sheer
pit of destruction opened, and victors and
vanquished fell headlong in.

But men look only a little way before and after; in the midst of evil, courage and gaiety shine brightest; hatred and love clothe men's hearts like a finely woven garment; and only God can weigh a deed and count it truly as glory or shame.

So Odysseus fought with the best, and better than any of them; and when it was a question of strategy or the ruses of war, there was no one to touch him. I will not tell you the tedious tale of those ten years, the famine, the disease, the slaughter, the savage hopes, the black despairs, which led to inevitable ruin; I will tell you only the end, for had it not been for Odysseus that end would not have been what it was: perhaps better, perhaps worse—who can say?

In the tenth year of the war Troy still held: hard pressed by hunger and the long siege, but undefeated. Priests and prophets had done their best to revive the failing hopes of the Greek armies by all the magic they knew. Troy could not fall, they said, without Philoctetes' bow. The bow was brought—but still

Troy stood. Steal from her shrine the sacred
image of Pallas, and the city will perish: the
image was stolen—Odysseus himself, with the
great fighter Diomed, undertook the almost
impossible task, entering the city by night disguised as a beggar—but Troy did not perish.
No breach could be made in her walls; her
supply lines eastward and northward to the
Black Sea and the Bosphorus could not be cut.
Dissension grew amongst the Greek commanders, and—worse than that—petty quarrels
born of the weariness and frustration of the
long campaign.

It was then, when Greek hopes were at their
lowest and failure seemed certain, that Odysseus went to Agamemnon and proposed his
plan.

"It's brains," he said, "are wanted to win
this war. Do as I advise, and the Trojans themselves will bring us into Troy—and we'll cut
their throats while they're asleep."

Agamemnon was angry, because he thought
Odysseus was mocking him. But Odysseus
forced him to listen.

"Build an image of wood," he said, "shaped like a horse, and cut on its flank the words: *To Pallas Athene from the Greeks: a thank offering for their safe return*. Then burn our camp, launch our ships, and sail westward toward home. The Trojans, seeing us gone, will drag the Horse into the city in triumph."

"You are a resourceful man, Odysseus; but these are the words of a fool."

Odysseus laughed.

"In the belly of the Horse," he said, "there will be fifty men, myself amongst them."

That night, at a council of the Greek commanders, Odysseus' plan was debated and found good.

At once the work began. Timber was felled on Mount Ida, and sawn into planks in a fold of the plain three miles from the city, where watchers from the walls could not see. Then Epeius, who was an architect and carpenter of skill and experience, was set to design the Horse and oversee its construction. It took weeks to build, and when finished was indeed a weird and monstrous beast, twenty feet high

at least from the bottom of its belly to the
ground, and hollow inside and as spacious as
a ship. They built a platform under its feet,
with wheels on it, so that a hundred men haul-
ing on hawsers could drag it along if they
pulled hard enough. On its right flank they
cut the inscription as Odysseus had told them.

The night of the attempt came, dark and
moonless. The horse was moved from its hiding place, hauled up to the city and left not
half a mile from the walls, to be full in view
when daylight came. Odysseus and his picked
companions, fifty strong, climbed on ladders
through the door in its belly, with their weapons, and wine to hearten them, a day's provisions and some coils of good rope, and the
door was shut.

Meanwhile in the camp by the sea preparations were going ahead for the feigned departure. Everything of value was put aboard the
ships, and the ships launched. Then the camp
itself—it had grown in all those years more like
a town than a camp, with wooden buildings as
fine as houses—was fired. The flames roared,

and the land breeze rolled the smoke over the sea, and in the smother of it the great fleet—all that was left of it—pulled away from the land.

They made for Tenedos, a few miles off shore, and there, under the lee of the island, they anchored and lay by, waiting for the signal to return—the beacon fire on the grave of Achilles, which Sinon the Trojan renegade was to kindle on the following night.

Dawn came: the solemn, tranquil, ageless dawn. In an instant the news ran through Troy that the Greeks had gone—fled away in the night—and the war was over. Life could begin again, warm and sweet as it used to be long ago, without the shadow of famine and fear and death.

The gates were flung open: people in hundreds streamed out on to the rolling plain, women amongst them, and children, laughing, chattering, shouting; and as the gay crowd spread toward the sea, the monstrous Horse watched it with his painted and ironic eye.

They gathered round the beast wondering.

They read the words cut in its side: *From the Greeks to Pallas Athene, an offering for their safe return.*

"Don't trust them," cried one.

"The Greeks are liars."

"Burn it."

"A gift in a Greek's hand is worse than a sword."

"Smash it to pieces."

A soldier flung his spear. As it struck the Horse there was a hollow sound, an ominous drum-note, and it stuck there quivering.

Just at that moment a patrol came back from the beach.

"Gone!" they cried. "The report is true."

"Every man of them—not a trace remains. Fled—vanished. Long live Troy!"

This confirmation of the news brought a fresh wave of excitement and joy to the crowd. Their suspicions of the Horse were forgotten. They shouted, they sang, they danced, they threw wreaths and garlands of flowers round the uncouth neck and legs of the absurd and monstrous image; hundreds of them laid hold of the ropes and hauled with all their might.

"An offering to Pallas!" they shouted.

"Drag it home!"

"Set it by her shrine! Victory, victory!"

A solitary voice was raised in protest; it was Cassandra, the princess, daughter of the king, the mad girl who could feel in her blood the coming of evil, but always warned in vain. Her cry of "Death" was drowned in the clamor; the Horse moved forward dragged by the straining ropes, swaying and jolting.

Inside was a muffled clang of arms, and Odysseus put his finger on his lips.

All that day, Troy's last, the rejoicing continued. In the bond of a common deliverance each man loved his neighbor, the poor were feasted at the tables of the rich, and prayers of thanksgiving rose to Gods who laughed at the folly and cruelty of men.

And all day the Wooden Horse stood within the walls, by the temple of Athene and the palace of the King.

The sun went down, and the traitor Sinon

lit the fire on Achilles' grave by the sea, to tell
the Greeks off Tenedos that Odysseus was in
Troy. With no word spoken the anchors were
hove in, and the ships stole silently back over
the darkening water. No picket, no patrol, no
sentry on the city walls saw them coming—
what need of watching when the war was over?
The army landed and with stealthy march
drew near to Troy.

Meanwhile in the city the noise of rejoicing
was growing less. Only the sound of scattered
voices, a snatch of song, a footfall in the street,
came to Odysseus' straining ears in the black
and stifling womb of the Horse, where he and
his companions waited.

Then silence. The city was secure in sleep.

Odysseus whispered: "Come." The bolts
were drawn back, the trapdoor opened, and
one by one the fifty men slid down the lowered
rope to the ground.

For a moment they stood doubtful. It was
eerie in the dark street, strange to be there, un-
molested, in the city which had defied them so
long. The sense of the sleepers was heavy on

them, and the guilt of blood not yet shed. A door in the palace, right above them, slammed softly in a draft of wind. Only death was awake.

Odysseus signed to three of his men. Together they slipped quickly away to the great gates in the western wall. There were guards at the gates, but their heads had fallen on their knees and their spears lay useless on the ground. Before they could wake, their throats were cut—luckier than most, in that they passed from sleep to death and knew no difference.

The gates were opened, and in less time than it takes to tell the city was full of armed soldiers as hungry as wolves for blood, or as men for revenge.

The story of the hours till dawn is not for me to tell. The sack of a city is a dreadful thing, and when men are hot for killing, glory and shame go hand in hand. Fire leapt, buildings blazed. Temple and tower went to the ground. Men who had snatched their arms, half-stupefied with terror and sleep, were massacred in the streets. The King himself was stabbed by his own altar stone; his palace gutted.

And what of Helen? It is said that before she was taken, Odysseus and Diomed saw her for an instant by the glare of flames, standing at a window of her house. Even then her spell touched them, as it had touched them long ago in the house of Tyndareus. For a moment they stood still, their hands dropped.

"No wonder that for such a woman we have endured and done so many dreadful deeds." The words formed themselves on Odysseus' lips, while the smoke and flame and blood seemed to swim like a mist before his eyes.

Few escaped. When dawn came the ancient and beautiful city was dust. In the cold, pure light the victors looked at each other with haggard eyes, wonderingly, as if they had awakened from a dream. Only the women were spared—the worse for them. As the sun rose for the new day, they were driven like sheep to the sea where the ships were waiting, never again to have a home.

{ Voyage to Lotus-Land }

THAT WAS HOW Troy fell, and it wasn't a pretty sight. The Greeks who destroyed it had to pay their price too; for few of them was life after the victory the life they had expected. Punishment, men say, is a lame dog and goes on three legs; but it comes up on a man in the end, and bites him. Many of them came to grief on the way home, what with wind and weather and bad seamanship, and were either drowned or forced to settle in some foreign country and build up a new life as best they could. As for Agamemnon, king of men, the very night he reached that fine house of his on the hills at Mycenæ, his wife killed him in his bath with a chopper.

But nobody killed Helen. She came in the end to queen it again in Argos with her rightful husband—but Helen was not like other women. People say she never even grew old.

For Odysseus the end of the war was a new beginning. Now at last he had all that his heart desired, and more.

It was time to go home. It isn't far from the beaches of Troy to Ithaca: a four days' voyage, perhaps, or five, with reasonable luck and a good crew. But how long did Odysseus take? Ten years—ten mortal years—as long again as the war itself. You'll say his luck was out. Well, that's as may be: it depends on what he wanted, and it's my belief that if every God on Olympus had conspired to bring him home with smooth seas and a soldier's wind and everything easy, there wouldn't have been a more disappointed man than he. It would have been years before he could go to sea again. A man can't, in decency, say goodbye to a wife without a moment's notice when she has waited for him through a war like that. There was the boy too: eleven years old and in need of discipline—and old Laertes mooning his time away amongst his vegetables and letting down the honor of his house. After all, Odysseus had a heart, despite appearances to the contrary.

No; when that first northerly blow came, Odysseus' luck was not out. It was in. Besides, when he did get home at last, what a story he had to tell! His son and Penelope no doubt exchanged a glance or two while he was telling it —but it is not polite to call one's father a liar, or one's husband either. Moreover, who knows that it wasn't all true? Stranger things come out of the sea than ever a landsman dreams of; and the sea itself is the most wonderful of them all.

It was good to be under way again. The twelve ships under Odysseus' command were dragged down the beach on rollers (heavy

work) and launched, and the men got aboard
and pulled over a calm sea to Tenedos. Here
they brought up for a refit; for nothing hurts
a ship so much as disuse and neglect, and the
years of war had opened their seams so that
they leaked like a basket, and peeled the paint
off them in ugly patches and turned their gay
vermilion bows to a dull rust.

The work was done with a will, for hearts
were high and the weather set fair—or so it
seemed.

Then, after a prayer to Poseidon, God of the
sea, they set sail, with a gentle southerly wind,
to cross the Ægean with its hundred islands to
Greece.

As darkness was falling they made the land
at Eubœa, not far from Aulis, where the expedition had started from at the beginning of
the war; and turned southward, pulling now,
for what wind there was, was against them,
and those old ships with their one square sail
were no good to windward—though they would
run, with the wind free, as fast and as safely as
the best of our own.

The night was overcast, and it soon fell
calm. As they coasted to the southward they
could hear the swell breaking on the jagged
and precipitous shore. Each ship carried a
lantern on the poop, so that they could keep
in company. All went well until at dawn on
the following day the whole fleet was off Cape
Malea at the southern extremity of Greece.
The sun came tardily up over a bank of cloud
to the east and north—a high dawn, as seamen
say—and was quickly swallowed again. There
was a heave on the sea, but not a ripple of
wind. Odysseus told his men, who had been
at the oars all night in successive watches, to
make more of an offing in case of trouble. It
was going to blow, but from which direction
it was hard to tell in these waters, where summer squalls are as capricious as they are violent. If it blew from the south, the ships would
be caught on a lee shore and in great danger.

Suddenly it hit them—whack, like the kick
of a mule—straight down from the mountains
behind Malea. Sailors' luck! that offing was
just what they didn't want. Had they con-

tinued to hug the coast they would have been under the lee of the land, and all well.

The ships were heeled by that first squall till their gunwales were nearly under. They were properly caught, and for a minute all was confusion. With a struggle, however, Odysseus got his vessel head to wind, and shouted to his men to pull for all they were worth to try to make the land. They pulled indeed, but it was useless: there was too much weight in the wind. The rest of the fleet was already driving before it to the southward.

Odysseus was compelled to follow them. The oars were laid in; Odysseus himself took the helm; a rag of sail was set to steady her, and the ship ran like a greyhound through the mounting seas.

In half an hour no land was to be seen: nothing but sky and sea—and even with those it took good eyes to tell where one began and the other ended, the ragged cloud-drift sweeping down on the gray tops of the marching waves.

Odysseus, seeing the alarm and disappoint-

ment in the faces of his men—they had expected to be home in a couple of days—
suddenly realized that he was enjoying himself. He began to sing, shouting above the
wind the remembered words of some song he
had heard—when? In the house of Tyndareus,
perhaps, from the lips of the ballad singers,
and the blacker the looks of his men, the
louder he sang. That first onset of the gale
filled him with exhilaration. Holding the
helm with all the strength of both his arms, he
kept the vessel running dead before wind and
sea, and as each wave mounted ever more
steeply astern, it was fine to feel how the ship
lifted to it, letting it run under her with a hiss
and roar, and never taking a drop aboard.
There was no doubt the Ithacan shipwrights
knew their job—she was a good vessel.

All that day it blew, and the following
night. As the sea increased, even the close-
reefed sail had to come in, and hawsers were
paid out astern to check the ship's way. The
fleet was scattered: it was each for himself
now.

A heavy blow will wear down any man's spirit in time, and by dawn on the second day even Odysseus grew glum. He began to hate the remorseless shrieking of the wind in the ship's rigging; his eyes ached with the spume in them, his body was exhausted by the violent and perpetual rolling, which made it impossible either to stand or lie or sit without every muscle tense. He was anxious too: none of the fleet was in sight, and the seas were so steep astern that every one of them looked as if it must break and overwhelm them.

At midday there was a shift of wind to the northwest, and the gale culminated in a vicious squall. Despite the hawsers astern and the two men on the steering oar, the ship broached-to: nothing could hold her. A green comber broke over her with a roar, half filling her hold, and everyone on board thought the next would finish her. But as luck would have it, the great wave was followed by a smooth, and the ship was got back on her course before the wind. Then—suddenly—the sun burst upon the sea. The glory of it was like a re-

prieve from death, and a minute later the
wind was gone, as suddenly as it had come.
The gale had blown itself out. Almost at the
same moment a man forward shouted: "Ship
ahoy!" and following his leveled arm, all on
board saw, not half a mile away, one—no, two
—of the other vessels of the fleet—then a third—
then three more. There they were, all round

the horizon, visible on the wave crests, sinking out of sight in the hollows, rolling their gunwales under—but safe.

Wine was served out to all hands, and sail was made. Presently they could see all the fleet following suit, and the sea was flowered with sails brilliant white in the sunshine. All hearts were high again.

Hardly was the square sail sheeted home before there was another shout from the lookout in the bows:

"Land ho!"

Eager eyes scanned the horizon ahead. There it was, a blue-gray line under the sun to the southward.

What land it was nobody knew. For thirty-six hours they had been running blind, and had sighted nothing since they drove past Cythera, Aphrodite's island, between Matapan and Malea. Cautiously the fleet—all together now, the whole dozen of them—closed with it, sailing easily with a new breeze from the nor'-west on their quarter, over a sea now rapidly going down and beginning to smile again like summer. Soon the misty blue of the coast turned to green, rising higher, and low, white houses could be seen amongst trees. Odysseus altered course to the westward, thinking it might be one of the innumerable islands of these seas; but after three hours' sailing the coast still stretched on unbroken. It was the mainland of the great southern continent of Africa.

Now with the weather so much improved, some of the men in Odysseus' ship were for altering course again to the northward in order to try for home as quickly as possible; and even Odysseus himself might have been willing to make a passage of it, hard though it was to resist the pleasure of setting foot on a strange shore and seeing what was to be seen. But the fact was they were short of water. Wine they still had in plenty, in big jars well stowed under the thwarts; but Greek wine is strong stuff, and though excellent to give a man a fillip in moments of danger or exhaustion, it doesn't do to quench his thirst. For that, it must be mixed with water.

This, then, decided them. Once more the ships were put about and coasted along as close inshore as Odysseus judged to be safe, until a cove was found with a sandy beach well protected from the swell by a promontory of rock. Here Odysseus ran his vessel ashore, and the rest of the fleet followed his lead.

The company disembarked, not forgetting their weapons, for there was no knowing what sort of reception they would receive. It was pleasant to be on land again after their rough passage, especially in so sweet a place—for there was on this coast a peculiar and delightful softness and fragrance in the air. It was a green and welcoming land. Indeed, Elpenor, one of the youngest of Odysseus' men and not too steady a character, was soon muttering to his neighbor that he, for one, wouldn't mind settling there for good and giving up the fools' game of seafaring. After all, why not. . .? However, he felt Odysseus' eye on him, and wisely said no more for the present.

They found a stream of fresh water bub-

bling out not far from the beach, and while
they were filling the water casks they were
surprised by the approach of two strangers.
The strangers, natives of the place, were un-
armed. They came to Odysseus, rightly guessing him to be the man in command, and in
the friendliest manner put to him the usual
questions.

"Who are you, strangers? What is your city
and the name of your parents? Why are you
voyaging? Are you pirates by any chance—or
some other sort of people?"

Odysseus made haste to assure the men that
his was by no means a pirate fleet. As to the
other questions, he was more guarded in his
answers; for he never thought it a good thing
to put too many cards on the table all at once.
So he merely said that he and his companions
had taken part in the famous siege of Troy,
and had been forced to this coast by stress of
weather.

He was surprised, and a little hurt, to learn
that these men, dark-skinned, mild-eyed, gentle creatures, had never even heard of the

siege, or of Troy either. This was odd, to say the least of it, and Odysseus asked somewhat haughtily what country this was that they had come to.

"Lotus-land," one of the strangers answered.

"We are the happiest people in the world, because we neither work nor worry."

At this there came a look into Odysseus' eye, as much as to say that he didn't think much of them on that account. But it wasn't worth trying to pick a quarrel about nothing, so he told his men to hurry up and get the water casks stowed aboard, for they mustn't waste the fine weather.

While this work was going on Elpenor and a couple of his friends slipped away with the two strangers, unobserved by Odysseus. Just as the ships were about to be hauled off into deep water, their absence was noticed by Polites, who was Odysseus' most trusted man.

"Elpenor!" he said. "The fellow's gone!"

"I might have guessed it," Odysseus answered. "That young man will come to no

good. And he's taken Eurylochus with him,
and that Mikkos."

A search party was at once organized under
Odysseus himself to round up the runaways.
They found them easily enough, in a village
not half a mile away, in a green hollow with a
stream running through it. The place was
cool with the breeze from the sea, and heavy
to fainting with the smell of flowers; the grass
was as soft as down to the feet, and the noise
of the stream was like sleep itself. Amongst the
low, leaf-thatched houses dark-skinned people moved as shyly and silently as fawns, and
a group of them, men and women, lay at their
ease by the stream. With them were Elpenor
and the two others. They looked as if they had
been there for ever, or as if time had suddenly
stood still.

Odysseus lowered his sword.

"Come," he said with unusual gentleness,
as if he mistrusted his own command. "The
ships are afloat. We are waiting for you."

For answer Elpenor held out to him a basket
of the fruit from which he and his friends

were eating—fine fruit, as big as mastic berries and as sweet as dates.

Odysseus stretched out his hand to the fruit, but drew it back.

"No . . ." he said. "No. . . ."

"Eat," Elpenor said.

"No."

But he reached out his hand again, and a faintness came over him, and it seemed that from all the people lying there between sleep and waking, and from the very ground itself and from the cool, bright air, came a sense of words that were yet not words, but an inexplicable longing in his heart.

"Eat the lotus fruit. Ithaca is far away; the sea is treacherous; endeavor is a dream. Eat the lotus fruit, and forget."

Then anger swept over him. Violently he dashed the basket from Elpenor's hand. "Seize him," he shouted. "And Mikkos—that fool—and Eurylochus. Tie him up—drag them off by the neck."

Odysseus' companions obeyed the command; the deserters were seized and dragged

back to the shore; and all the way, though
they had seen unmoved the horror of a ten
years' war, the three of them wept like children. Then they were bundled aboard Odysseus' ship, and shoved under the thwarts with
their arms and ankles tied, and the fleet put
to sea again.

{ Polyphemus }
{ and Nobody }

Now with a good chart and a compass and a pair of parallel rulers most fools could set a course from the African coast to any island in the Ægean or Ionian sea. But without any of these things, I have no doubt it is a ticklish business. Besides, nobody knew on what part of the coast they were.

They were properly lost, and every man in the fleet looked to Odysseus to solve their puzzle. That Ithaca lay to the northward was

plain enough; but to the east of north, or
west? and how much? It may be that Odysseus
had an inkling of the matter; for there are
some seamen who can find their way over
oceans like eels to their breeding grounds—
and Odysseus was one of them. But, be that
how it may, the fact is that he steered westward for a stretch. Perhaps he thought he'd
pick up better winds that way—I don't pretend to an opinion.

One night, after three or four days at sea,
the weather came on thick. It was black dark
besides; not a breath of wind, and a long swell
running. So far as they could, the twelve vessels kept together in a bunch, for company's
sake—though it was a job to see the poop lantern even of the nearest ship—and rowed easy,
the men singing to keep their spirits up. Elpenor and Eurylochus and little Mikkos had
had their straps cut by now, but were still feeling ashamed of themselves.

Suddenly, without warning, the leading
vessel, which was Odysseus', ran aground with
a wallop, and a moment later (as was obvious

from the shouts of alarm and the babel of all
sorts of contradictory orders) the remainder
of the fleet did the same. Nobody could see
any ship but his own, except the glim of a
light or two in the fog, and everyone supposed
he was done for. However, for a reason they
could not understand, there was no longer any
swell, and the ships having hit the bottom,
didn't bump as might have been expected,
but lay as still as if they'd been on the stocks.

The only thing to do was to take a line
ashore and wait for daylight.

When daylight came and the dawn breeze
had dispersed the fog, what was everyone's
astonishment to find that they had run, by
pure luck, into the most perfect natural harbor you can imagine. It was an inlet in an
island, protected by two ridges of rock and
running in to a sandy beach—the sort of place
where a ship could lie as quiet as a mouse
without even an anchor down. What's more,
there was a stream of fresh water close to the
shore, plenty of timber, and (by the noise they
were making) thousands of wild goats every-

where. Nothing could be better for hungry
and thirsty men.

It wasn't long before half a dozen goats for
each ship were roasting and a jar of the best
wine broached. Indeed, most of that day was
spent in the pleasures of the table, if I may so
call it.

Now while they were lounging at ease on
the island, they had been watching with interest certain signs of habitation on the mainland to the southward, which was not more
than a mile distant. Smoke was rising at scattered points, and now and then it even seemed
that they could catch on the wind the sound
of hoarse voices, apparently human, and the
bleating of sheep.

At dawn therefore on the following day,
Odysseus announced that he would go over to
the mainland in his own ship with his own
crew, and that the remainder would stay
where they were and wait for news.

"Perhaps," he said, "they are hospitable
people who are tending those fires. But perhaps they are not."

On reaching the coast, Odysseus chose the eleven best men from his crew and, telling the rest to stay on guard by the ship, went off inland to explore. He took some food with him and a big bottle of a special brand of strong and delicious wine, of which he still had a little left.

Soon they came to a cave cut in the rock, with a stone wall round it to make an enclosure, evidently for cattle. They marched boldly in. Nobody was at home—no human being that is, but there were lots of kids and young lambs in pens, and any amount of pails full of whey, and baskets of cheeses. Clearly the owner of the place, whoever he was, liked to do himself well.

Most of the men thought the obvious thing to do was to take as many cheeses as they could carry, drive the lambs and kids down to the ship, and make off back to their island. Voyagers must live—and here was a grand chance of provisioning the ships with no expense. Odysseus, however, would not allow this; he was curious to find out who it was that lived

in the cave. They did, however, take just a few
cheeses—enough to make a small meal for
their present need—and then settled themselves down in the cave to wait for their host.

About sundown he came. One glance at
him was enough to make Odysseus wish he
had taken his friends' advice, and to remember the old saying that it was curiosity that
killed the cat. He was a terrible fellow eight
feet high and as strong as an elephant, with a
mouth as big as a horse collar, and shark's
teeth, and one flaming eye as round as a wheel.
He stalked into the cave, driving his sheep
before him, flung down a great faggot of fire-
wood he was carrying and closed the entrance
tight with a rock which weighed a ton.

Odysseus and his friends scuttled away into
a dark recess at the back of the cave, and
crouched there to await developments, not
feeling happy.

Polyphemus the Cyclops (for that's who it
was) milked his goats as calm as you please,
and then lit his fire. Directly the flame spurted,
he saw he had visitors.

"Ho, ho," he said, "and who are you? Pirates? Or are you just respectable merchants? Where do you come from, eh?"

Odysseus—the only one of the party who had presence of mind to answer—hastened to assure the Cyclops of their peaceful intention.

"We are only paying a call," he said. "I trust, kind sir, you will remember the duties of a host. God sends guests, and protects them too."

"God?" said the Cyclops. "What's Zeus to me, or any other God? I've no use for fairy tales."

With this, he reached out his hairy arm, seized two of Odysseus' men by the ankles, picked them up as if they were puppies and knocked their brains out against the floor. Then he pulled them to bits and ate them, bone and all. After that he drank a pailful of milk and went to sleep, thoroughly pleased with himself.

Now Odysseus, though a rare hand at getting into trouble, was equally good at getting out of it. Even at this moment, when his nine

surviving companions were gibbering in helpless fright, he had a plan ready. He could have
killed the Cyclops then and there as he slept;
but what would have been the use? They'd
only have died of slow starvation in the cave,
unable to move that enormous rock which
shut them in. He had a much better idea.

He heartened his friends as well as he could
and told them to wait till morning. Morning
came, and the Cyclops, after eating two more
Greeks for breakfast, pushed away the door-
stone and went out for his day's work with his
flocks. Unhappily he replaced the rock immediately he was outside—thinking, no doubt, of
that evening's supper.

Odysseus, however, had noticed on the previous night the trunk of an olive tree—green
wood—lying on the floor of the cave: a fine
piece of timber, as big as a ship's mast, which
the Cyclops had presumably cut to serve him
as a walking stick as soon as the sap was out of
it. Directly the Cyclops was gone (they could
hear him whistling as he went off down the
hill with his sheep), Odysseus set his men to

chop a six-foot length from the tree trunk and smooth it carefully. Then he himself sharpened one end of it to a point and hardened it off in the embers of the fire which was still glowing. This done, he hid the sharpened stake under a pile of sheep dung, and waited for evening.

At the same hour as before the Cyclops returned.

"Ho, ho," he said, "I still have my visitors, I see."

The men cowered back into their corner. But it was no good: two more were selected, and the Cyclops had his horrid supper as before.

When he had finished, Odysseus plucked up his courage and began to execute his plan. First he filled a bowl with the strong, sweet wine out of the bottle he had brought from the ship.

"Cyclops," he said, "I brought this wine specially for you, hoping we might drink together and be friends. You are a cruel monster; but drink it all the same, and see what generous men we Greeks are."

The Cyclops drank the bowlful at a gulp, and asked for more. It was very good wine, and he liked it. He drank three bowls full—and began to nod. However, he was not quite drunk yet, only mellow.

"Stranger," he said, "tell me your name. This wine is a remarkable vintage. I'd like to give you a present in return."

"My name," Odysseus answered, "is Nobody."

"Nobody? That's good. I'll eat you last, Mr. Nobody. That shall be your present."

At that instant the wine got the better of the Cyclops; he tumbled face upwards on the ground with an almighty crash, and lay there snoring, his neck twisted askew.

This was what Odysseus was waiting for. He quickly fetched out the sharpened stake from under the dung-heap, and heated its point to a glow in the ashes of the fire. Then he thrust it with all his weight into the Cyclops' eye, leaning on it mightily, while the others got a thong round it and spun it this way and that, like men drilling a hole in a ship's timber. In went the hot point, and the blood bubbled and boiled and hissed round it, with much the same noise an axe-head makes when a smith plunges it red-hot into water to temper it.

Polyphemus gave a frightful yell and began to roar for help to the other Cyclops who lived round about.

"What on earth's the matter?" they said, coming and listening at the door of the cave.

"It's Nobody's treachery. . . . Nobody is killing me . . ." the Cyclops howled.

"Then that's all right," came the answer. "You must be ill, and we can't do anything about that." And off they went again.

Polyphemus, still making a dreadful din because of the pain, groped his way to the door stone of the cave and pushed it away; but to prevent his enemies' escape he sat in the opening with his great arms held wide.

So near, and yet so far! Once again Odysseus had to rack that quick brain of his to think of a way of getting past those terrible, clutching hands.

In less than no time he'd hit on it: by the light of the still glowing fire he lashed together fifteen rams in threes; fine animals with thick, black fleeces. Then he told his five remaining companions that when dawn came each must sling himself under the belly of the middle ram of three, cling on for dear life, and let the animals carry him out. He himself would do the same with the ram who was pick of the flock, a powerful great beast and Polyphemus' favorite. Then there was nothing to be done but wait for daylight.

At last it came—the blessed sun. The rams and sheep were eager to get out to pasture and began to stream out of the cave, past the Cyclops, who was still sitting in the doorway, moaning with rage and pain. Quickly Odysseus' men did as they had been bidden, hung on tight to the thick fleece under the rams' bellies, and started their perilous ride. As each ram passed, Polyphemus felt its back with his hand, knowing him by touch, and sent him on

with a spank behind. He never once thought
of feeling underneath.

Lastly Odysseus himself took a powerful
grip on his own chosen beast, twisting his fin-

gers deep into the soft fleece, and hung there
upside-down like a bat. The ram trotted to
the doorway, and out came the Cyclops' hand
to feel him. Well Polyphemus knew at the first
touch that this ram was his darling, leader of

his flock, who was always first out when morning came.

"O my best ram, my dear one," he groaned;
"what is the matter? Why are you last to leave
the cave? Can it be you are in grief because of
your master's eye? Ah, if you could only tell
me where Nobody is hiding!"

But not that time either did the Cyclops
think of putting his hand underneath. He
hadn't enough sense.

So Odysseus and his five friends escaped
from the cave, and mighty glad they were of
it. They hurried down to the ship, driving
their rams and as many sheep as they could
muster, and scrambled aboard. Just as they
were pushing off, they saw the Cyclops on the
cliff-edge above the beach; then, hardly was
the ship clear when he picked up an enormous
rock and flung it. The rock crashed into the
sea a yard ahead of Odysseus' ship, and the
wave it set up swept her back almost on to the
sand. Odysseus seized a pole and shoved like
mad, and got her off again; and as the ship
once more began to move, he yelled in tri-

umph at the Cyclops: "If you want to know who it really was who put out your eye, you beast, it was Odysseus, son of Laertes, the Ithacan, the sacker of cities."

In rage Polyphemus tore up another boulder as big as a hill, and hurled it. It whirled through the air and came smash into the sea hardly an inch from Odysseus' rudder. This time, however, the mountainous wave of its falling pushed them in the right direction—away from the beach. The rowers pulled with all their might, and in another minute were out of danger.

The rest of that day was spent on the island, resting and eating—for they had a splendid supply of good meat to roast. Odysseus was pleased with himself. It was bad to have lost six men; but still, it might have been worse. Amongst his company, however, there were certain misgivings. No commander could be braver or more resourceful than Odysseus: that went without saying. But he was rash—he took chances—and they didn't altogether like it.

It was Eurylochus who gave voice to the uneasiness.

"Odysseus," he said, "there's a tale that the Cyclops is a son of Poseidon, God of the sea."

"What of it?" Odysseus answered.

"Poseidon will be angry. He'll raise storms to drown us—we'll never get home."

"Don't be a fool," Odysseus said, and, rolling himself up in his blanket, settled down for a comfortable night.

How to Deal
with an Enchantress

Whether it was Poseidon who was responsible for the frightful disasters which followed, or just plain human stupidity, I don't pretend to determine. Believe as you please.

They left the island of Æolia, which was their next port of call, in high spirits and pretty confident of getting home without undue delay. Æolus, who lived there in great luxury, had entertained them for a month on

the fat of the land, and, at parting, had given
Odysseus a leather bag in which, so he said,
all the winds were shut up except the one they
needed to blow them home. Odysseus had
kept pretty quiet about this bag, refusing to
satisfy the curiosity of his men about what was
inside it. This was annoying, and led to all
sorts of guesses, some of them by no means
complimentary to their commander. Suppose
—for instance—it was treasure, which Odysseus
wanted to keep to himself, instead of sharing
it out as an honorable captain should do?

For nine days all went well. Odysseus himself hadn't slept a wink: indeed, he had been
at the helm continuously night and day, refusing all offers of relief. On the tenth morning they were actually in sight of the shining
cliffs of Ithaca, when Odysseus, worn out, suddenly and most unfortunately fell fast asleep.

Now was the men's chance to have a peep
into that bag. They opened it, and at that very
instant a most appalling squall hit them, bang
out of the blue. As for the bag, there was no
time even to think of it any longer, for it was

a case of all hands to get the square sail in before it was blown to rags, or the ship turned turtle.

That squall was the beginning of a gale which hopped all round the compass, and finally settled in the east and blew like smoke for over a week.

As luck would have it the first land they made when the wind eased was the same island they had sailed from, Æolia. None of the company was in very good shape, so Odysseus called on Æolus again in the hope of further assistance. He had a chilly reception; and when he confessed that his men had opened the precious bag, Æolus would have nothing more to do with him, and sent him away with a flea in his ear.

Now that was bad enough; but it was nothing to what was coming next. The fleet sailed —short of provisions and the men in bad heart. They carried on for six days and then sighted land. As they closed with it, Odysseus had a strong premonition of danger—and it would have been well for their crews had the cap-

tains of the other ships shared it. But so eager
were they to stretch their legs ashore and lay
in a provision of meat and water, that all
eleven of them took their vessels without a
thought of anything else straight into a little
circular basin on the coast, surrounded with
high cliffs, and obviously an excellent anchor-
age. Odysseus, however, felt his way cautiously
inshore, and brought up outside the basin,
with lines ashore to the rocks.

It wasn't long before Odysseus' caution was
justified. Before the crews of the vessels in the
basin had had time to get ashore, a horde of
ferocious giants, almost as big as Cyclops and
quite as savage, appeared on the ring of cliffs
and began pelting the ships below with huge
and jagged boulders. The ships lying all in a
bunch made an easy mark, and were smashed
to bits in less than no time. Those of the men
who were not smashed too were speared like
fish as they desperately swam in the deep
water. Every one of them—and there were
nearly five hundred—was killed.

But Odysseus got away—the savages were

too much occupied with their sport in the basin even to have noticed his ship. So with the shrieks of his unfortunate comrades still ringing in his ears, he cut his ropes, and his crew pulled for all they were worth out to sea and safety.

This dreadful disaster had a depressing effect on the survivors—only one ship out of the fleet of twelve which had sailed so gallantly and hopefully from Troy—one ship and her crew of forty-five. However, as all adventurers must, they had to make the best of it.

By now, even Odysseus was extremely doubtful of his whereabouts. To be sure, he had brought his fleet successfully from Æolia to within sight of Ithaca, so why—you may ask —couldn't he do the same from this land of savages, which was, after all, only six days' sail away? The trouble was that Æolia was one of those floating islands, of which there were plenty in those days. One never knew where it would be; and when they were driven back to it by the gale, it might well have been leagues and leagues away from its original position. In fact, it was a pure fluke that they had met it again at all.

All Odysseus could do, therefore, was to set a course by guess work—and not mention his doubts to his companions.

They were down to their last drop of water and their last strip of dried mutton before they made land again.

The land (as one might expect) turned out to be an island. A little cautious reconnoitering revealed that it was inhabited; for somewhere in the middle of it, from amongst a tuft of trees, smoke was rising.

Odysseus, remembering the savages at their last port of call, did not think it was advisable for the whole ship's company to approach the house—if house it was—where the smoke was coming from; so he divided his men into two parties, putting one under Eurylochus and taking charge of the other himself. Then they drew lots to decide which party should go.

The lot fell to Eurylochus. Eurylochus didn't like the job, nor did his men; but there was nothing for it, so off they had to go. Odysseus and his party waited by the ship for news.

The news came all too soon. The first thing Odysseus saw was Eurylochus himself pelting back toward the beach, all alone, his eyes popping out of his head with fright.

"What on earth's the matter?" said Odysseus.

"Pigs," Eurylochus gasped. "They're all turned into pigs!"

Odysseus asked him somewhat severely to explain himself, and mumbled something about a good many of them being more than half pigs already.

"But really pigs," Eurylochus panted in great distress; "with b-bristles. . . ."

This sounded serious, and indeed it was; for when Eurylochus had got his breath, he went on to explain how he and his party had gone to the tuft of trees where the smoke was, and found there a fine castle built of stone. They called for admittance, and the door was opened by a beautiful woman—or rather not by a beautiful woman but by a most horrible witch, which is sometimes (strangely enough) the same thing. They all went in at the witch's invitation, except Eurylochus, who smelt trouble and stayed outside. Five minutes later his poor friends were all pigs.

Odysseus (who had a fund of knowledge denied to ordinary men) knew at once that the beautiful witch must be the famous Circe. But he had no intention of being defeated by a mere enchantress, so he at once made up his mind what to do.

"Eurylochus," he said, "we must go and

rescue them. Show me the way to the castle."

"I can't," Eurylochus said.

"Can't?"

"I daren't."

Still goggling with fright, he begged Odysseus to put to sea at once with the men that remained, leaving the rest to their fate. Odysseus treated this suggestion with the contempt it deserved, and told Eurylochus he was a coward. There was nothing for it but to go alone.

He set off at once—sorry, indeed, for his poor friends who had been turned into pigs, but burning with curiosity to see Circe. He felt pretty sure that she wouldn't turn *him* into a pig provided he acted boldly and took the initiative.

Charms, however, are pretty powerful things, so as he happened to notice a root or two of a certain plant called moly, which he knew had a strong antidotal influence, he pulled one up and took it with him, just in case.

Arrived at the castle, he called for admittance just as the others had done. The polished door was opened, and Circe herself welcomed him in. Everything inside was of the finest quality: wooden settles rubbed bright, chairs picked out in silver, embroidered footstools, rich purple rugs, baskets of gold for fruit, silver drinking cups, and four beautiful maid-servants. What a place for a sea-weary sailor!

Circe made him sit on one of the silvery chairs, and at once mixed him a bowl of something to drink. But what, exactly, did it contain? Ah, that was the danger. . . . However, feeling the antidote in the fold of his tunic, Odysseus, keeping his eye on Circe all the time, drank it boldly down. Then he leapt from his chair, drew his sword, and advanced upon the enchantress as if he would chop her head off.

He couldn't have hit on a better method of procedure. Indeed, that is exactly the right way to treat a witch. Circe was terrified; she fell on her knees under the threatening sword and begged Odysseus to have mercy.

"But who can you be?" she said; "I have

never before met a man who could resist my spells. Surely there is only one on earth capable of *that*—Odysseus, son of Laertes."

Then she told Odysseus that she did not really intend him any harm at all; on the contrary, she loved him dearly—a declaration which Odysseus received with a certain reserve. However, he allowed Circe to provide a bath for him (much needed after his many days at sea), and to dress him in beautiful new clothes, and serve him a substantial meal. But he refused to taste the food until he had exacted a promise from the enchantress.

"Circe," he said, "you cannot expect a commander to settle down to a banquet when half his men have been turned into pigs. It would be heartless. So before I have even a bite, you must restore them to their proper shape."

Now it is easy to turn a man into a pig, but much more difficult to turn a pig back into a man. Circe, however, was a very great enchantress, and managed it without trouble. Presently Odysseus had the pleasure of seeing all twenty-two of his men walk into the hall, looking their proper selves again—though a few of them were a trifle shamefaced, and unwilling to meet Odysseus' eye.

Then they had their banquet together, and a magnificent banquet it was.

When it was finished, Circe told Odysseus that he must not think of going away for a long time yet: on the contrary, he must fetch the rest of his men who were waiting by the ship with Eurylochus, and she would entertain the whole ship's company for as long as they pleased. Odysseus agreed. He had no further fear of Circe—for once you have started on the right lines with a witch, you can do pretty well what you please with her—so off he went back to the beach.

Eurylochus was astonished to see him. Indeed he was almost angry at the sight of his cheerful face.

"However did you escape?" he stammered.

Odysseus answered that it was easy enough: a matter of that kind called only for a little resolution and common sense.

"And what's more," he added, "not only are

the rest of your party perfectly all right again, but the whole lot of us—you included—are going to Circe's house for a long stay. We could all do with a little luxury after what we have been through."

"I won't go," Eurylochus said.

"Still frightened?"

"Certainly not; but—nothing would induce me."

"All right," Odysseus said cheerfully; "then stay here by yourself. It's all one to me."

The other men were delighted with the prospect of visiting Circe's grand house, and started gaily off with Odysseus. Eurylochus watched them go, scowling. When the last of them was a hundred yards away, he could bear it no longer. He followed—after all, nothing is worse than being called a coward. Besides, he was hungry.

So successfully had Odysseus got the better of Circe's dangerous qualities that she proved a charming hostess. The ship's company stayed with her for a whole year, and never showed the least sign of turning into pigs, either by

Circe's enchantments or their own piggish propensities. It was a most enjoyable visit and a great refreshment after the perils and hardships of the sea.

But at last the time came when many of the men began once more to think longingly of home. For once, it was left to others to propose to Odysseus the continuation of the voyage— which shows how much more agreeable he had found Circe than might have been expected.

Odysseus consented to go, and regretfully told Circe of his decision.

"And perhaps," he added, "out of the power of your many enchantments, you will help us on our voyage, by giving us a fair wind, or something of that sort. For the voyage is likely to prove a difficult one."

"I would gladly do so if I could," Circe replied; "but a man's fate is written before he is born, and you, Odysseus, are not fated to reach Ithaca just yet. You still have many adventures before you."

Odysseus was silent. He had a strong feeling that Circe was right, and he was wondering whether or not it would be advisable to tell his crew what she had said. On the whole he thought he had better not, for nothing endangers a voyage like a disheartened crew. As for himself, having once decided to break with the comfortable life in Circe's beautiful island, he found he was itching for the sea again.

The very next day the voyagers said goodbye and went aboard—all except poor Elpenor, who had got drunk in the excitement of preparing for departure, climbed up to the roof of the castle and fallen asleep. Waking with a start, he had forgotten the ladder, stepped over the edge and broken his neck.

{ Beyond the World's Edge }

Odysseus was now really and truly out of all his bearings. He hadn't the smallest notion of what course he should set for home. Naturally, he didn't mention this to his men, not wishing to destroy their confidence, such as it was. I would tell you myself where Circe's island was, if I could; but it would be idle to pretend that I know any better than Odysseus did. It seems probable, however, from what happened next, that he was

already far into the Western Ocean, in a part
of the world beyond the sunset which no
Greek sailor before him had ever dreamed of,
let alone visited.

You doubtless know that Ocean is a vast
river which encircles the earth, and that what
lies on its farther shore is one of the greatest of
mysteries. Now Odysseus, when Circe's island
was five or six days astern, had reason to believe, or at any rate to guess, that if he held on
as he was going he would somehow or other
reach this shore. It was clear to him that they
were no longer in the familiar Grecian Sea,
because the farther they sailed the longer the
nights became and the shorter the days; there
was a dreary chill in the wind, the marching
seas rolled endlessly up, forbidding, gray, and
cold; mists came swirling down, and the sun,
if they saw him at all, was small and rayless.

They sailed for many weeks, and at last the
sun went out altogether and there was darkness. Nothing could be seen but a few stars between the scud, and the glimmering wave
crests. Fear was in the heart of every man of the

vessel's crew, draining his blood away; but Odysseus kept them at the work of the ship, as a captain must, or perish. I do not doubt that even he was afraid, though mixed with his fear was a fierce exultation that he had brought his ship to such a place, and still lived.

At last they came to land, knowing of its presence by the dull roar of breakers, that sound which of all others is the most dreadful to seamen. They closed with it in the darkness, and some God must have guided them in; for the ship was not smashed, but came safely ashore upon the sand.

Doubtful, and all but spent, the weary men disembarked. A dark continent stretched before them, fog-bound, wind-wracked, sunk in perpetual and Cimmerian night. It was a place of terror and gloom, haunted by ghosts and full of whispering like the voices of the dead. The men huddled together for comfort and company; they muttered prayers to whatever gods they knew, offering a sheep as a blood sacrifice, cutting its throat and letting the blood fall upon the ground. Then they fell into an uneasy sleep.

To Odysseus, as he lay on that wild coast, there came fancies more vivid than dreams and stranger than truth. Again and again he started up, his hand on his sword hilt, his eyes wide; but nothing was there but the humped bodies of his friends, tossing in sleep, and beyond them the darkness.

But the visions persisted. The night was full of eyes, faces, forms. They crowded about him, thick as leaves, dissolving and taking shape again, wraiths of darkness, phantom bodies. In the presence of them Odysseus was filled with an anguish he couldn't understand; a helpless pity, a mortal fear. He tried to beat them off, but could not. They pressed closer, countless thousands of them, their lips moving as if they would speak. Who or what they were, Odysseus did not know, until suddenly from the spectral dance one figure detached itself and floated clear before him. It was Anticleia, his mother; and in that instant Odysseus knew that she was dead.

The figure faded, and then it seemed that there was a sound of words in his ears, and another presence, more urgent than the first, was telling him to listen, that he might learn the secrets of what the future held. A trance was on him, and he was freed from the barrier of flesh and saw at that moment as a God sees, present and past and future as one. He saw his home in rocky Ithaca, the sunny garden, the remembered rooms. Penelope was there, and Telemachus his son, fast growing to manhood. He saw the fig tree on the wall. And he knew that all was not well. Penelope was true, and loved him still; but danger threatened—he could see it gathering like a cloud far away, and growing, till it would burst and overwhelm all that he loved, if he were not there.

He struggled to fling the vision off; but other phantoms pressed on him, ghosts of men and women long dead, Alcmene and Iphimedeia, Orion the hunter, and Achilles himself, whom Odysseus with his own eyes saw killed at Troy. At the sight of them he was filled with pain for the sorrowfulness of our mortal lot, in which glory and delight so quickly pass into the darkness which waits for all. Thicker and thicker the phantoms gathered, innumerable as swallows in autumn before they fly over the sea, until Odysseus could bear it no longer. He started to his feet, as if to fight them away; and suddenly they were gone, and he was left with his sleeping companions, the dark coast, the dismal wind, the drumbeat of the surf on the sand, and the longing for the sun which would not come.

He roused his crew, and more dead than alive they got the ship into the water and made an offing, only too thankful to be out of that dreadful place. All of them, it seems, had been afflicted with terrible dreams while they slept, and Eurylochus and little Mikkos were convinced that they had sailed straight into Hell. Perhaps they had. Hell's an easy place to go to —though I never before heard of a man sailing his ship there. However, that's as may be. As for Odysseus, he expressed no opinion, but kept his thoughts to himself.

When they had got their offing, the current

of the River of Ocean carried them swiftly
along until once again they were in the wide
spaces of the sea. The sail was set and the oars
unshipped, and at last after a weary length of
time the sun rose above a bank of mist and
grew steadily in strength and brightness until
the sea was blue again. So great was the joy and
refreshment he brought that it was almost like
being at home.

It was a joy, however, which did not last
long. The greatest pleasure is relief from pain;
and when the pain is forgotten, the pleasure
soon goes too. So it was that Odysseus' crew
began to grumble: secretly at first amongst
themselves, then more openly, then with
threats of mutiny and violence against their
commander if he didn't bring them soon into
waters which they knew.

But what was the good of it? Not a man
amongst them had a notion of the ship's position, and if they had pitched Odysseus overboard they wouldn't have starved or drowned
any more slowly—more quickly, very likely,
for they all knew in their heart of hearts that

Odysseus was the only real sailor on board, and that if anyone could bring them home again, he was the man.

Moreover, Odysseus himself was now, for the first time, desperately anxious to be home. He couldn't get out of his head the strange experiences he had had in the Dark Land, and anxiety about his wife and family began to gnaw at him. For years he had given them hardly a thought; he had followed the lead of his own reckless and adventurous spirit, both during the war and after, grasping with both hands what luck threw in his way, good and bad alike, and let the old life go hang. Now he knew that wouldn't do. What happens when a man is away from home for ten years—or twelve—or fifteen? His son was only a boy, and Laertes was old and getting queer in the head besides: even before the war he had done no public business in the island, but lived like a recluse, with little interest but his herbs and flowers. And Penelope—Penelope was good, and to be trusted; but what if she thought he was dead? There would be plenty of people in

Ithaca and elsewhere to persuade her of that; and after so long it wouldn't be difficult to believe. And what then. . .? After all, it was Ithaca and home, in spite of all else, which he loved best in the world; and it was slipping from him. Dangers were gathering—he was certain of it, with a knowledge like prophecy.

These uncomfortable thoughts, added to the task of keeping his muttering and unruly men in order, made the present voyage a misery. Once it gets inside a man's defenses, nothing is more hateful than the sea, and for the first time in his life Odysseus hated it, and had a hard task to keep a brave face toward his men.

How long they sailed I don't know, but it was mighty long. At last, however, either by pure luck or because Odysseus, when he wanted to, really could find his way as the fish do across the pathless seas, by keeping an easterly course they came again to Æææ—or Sunrise Island as it is called. Here Circe welcomed them like long-lost friends, and good food and drink and fresh water in abundance revived their spirits and made the past seem like a bad dream. This time nobody was turned into a pig, and they did not prolong their stay, but were soon off again, refreshed and hopeful, with a fine store of provisions on board.

Before they sailed, Circe gave Odysseus a few sailing directions and some excellent advice. She told him to beware of the Sirens, and on no account to land on the coast which they inhabited; for though they had the voices of angels they were demons and would eat him. She told him to give a berth to the Clashing Rocks, should he choose the route in which they lay; for though the passage between them looked safe enough from a distance, once a ship was fairly in it the rocks rushed together and ground it to bits. She told him he would need all his resolution in the Straits, where on one side lurked Scylla the man-eating monster, and on the other Charybdis, a frightful whirlpool waiting to suck him down. And lastly she told him of a herd of cattle on the island of Thrinacie which he must on no account molest; for these cattle were sacred, and whoever killed them, even in the direst stress of hunger, would certainly come to a dismal end.

Once more they set sail, a happier crew than had left the Dark Land; for now they were hopeful again, and the return to Æææ had restored their confidence in their commander. The land of the Sirens was safely past, despite the intolerable sweetness of their beckoning voices, and with a fair wind and a smooth sea all went well until they drew near the Straits.

Odysseus had not mentioned Scylla and Charybdis to his men, for he was afraid of the effect that the prospect of passing them might have upon the crew. He knew from experience that anticipation of danger is often worse than danger itself—and he was not going to risk it.

The first thing they saw as they approached the Narrows was broken water on their starboard hand, with a cloud of driven spume hanging above it like smoke. The hiss and roar of it was audible a mile away. In a rip like that it was obvious that no ship could live. The men were so scared that they dropped their oars, and for a minute or two there was a most unseaman-like flurry and confusion, with the vessel drifting broadside-on and out of control.

All Odysseus' presence of mind was needed to restore order. "Men," he cried, "this isn't the first bit of trouble we've been in together! I've got you out before, and I'll get you out again. Come, let's see what you're made of— and obey orders. All together now—pull! Man at the helm, keep her over to port. Hug the cliff there and give the tide rip all the berth you can, or it'll suck us in and drown us."

The men obeyed—for there is nothing like a firm order to bring a frightened crew to their senses. Way was got on the ship again, and quickly—all too quickly—she entered the Narrows. Not a man could keep his eyes off that boiling cauldron of water as the ship swept by —it was horrible. In the suck of the sea it seemed that the very sand at the bottom was exposed to view, and in the surge of it the spray was flung as high as the top of the cliff.

Odysseus, however, wasn't bothering overmuch about the tide rip, fearsome though it was. Having satisfied himself that the man at

the helm was obeying his orders, he kept all his attention on the sheer face of the cliff on the opposite side. Somewhere in a cranny of that cliff the monster Scylla was waiting for them. Odysseus dared not warn his crew of the danger—if he did, ten to one they'd drop their oars again and hide under the foredeck, and the ship would be drawn into the whirlpool after all. He said nothing, but though he watched

the cliff till his eyes ached, he couldn't see a
thing.

A cheer from the men told him that Charybdis was safely astern. Odysseus turned to look,
and at that very instant the six vile necks of
Scylla slid like snakes out of an invisible slit in
the cliff, writhed downward in a flash, and
snatched up six of the crew.

The poor fellows shrieked; and when Odysseus turned again, there were their arms and
legs dangling in the air over his head.

"Odysseus!" they screamed. But not even
Odysseus could help them then. In two minutes they were crunched up, bones and all.

The Straits were passed, but at what a cost!
Sick with horror, the remaining company,
with scarcely strength to pull on the oars,
watched their vessel sweep out on the tide into
the blue, calm water of the open sea. Odysseus
gave the order to make sail; it was sullenly
obeyed, with many black looks and mutterings; some swore under their breath that if
they were lucky enough to get home, they
would never ship with Odysseus a second time

—it was too risky. He attracted disasters as a ripe fig attracts flies. Foolhardy—that's what he was; and his passion for finding out things which were better left alone wasn't decent. Why had he sailed through those accursed straits at all, instead of taking the safe passage to the southward? Whose fault was it that they had spent those terrible months in the lost oceans of the south and west, if not his? He had sailed them to the shores of Hell, just for the fun of it, to satisfy his curiosity. That was the sort of man he was—he, who thought himself so clever. And ten to one, Eurylochus was right about Poseidon—that trick their captain was so proud of, which he had played on the Cyclops, had angered the God, and he was pursuing Odysseus with disaster until every man of them was dead.

Odysseus was well aware of the mutterings against him; but they didn't trouble him much. He knew (and knew that his men knew) that he was the only competent navigator in the ship, and that nobody else stood a chance of bringing her home. To mutiny, and pitch him overboard, would be to destroy their one hope of ultimate safety—and not even they would be fools enough for that.

Nevertheless, he thought it wise to give his men rest and refreshment and a chance to recover their spirits at the earliest opportunity. The opportunity came toward sundown that same day, when they closed with the island of Thrinacie. Odysseus himself, remembering Circe's warning about the cattle, would much have preferred to give the island a berth and sail on; but under the circumstances he judged it better to risk trouble with the cattle than face the certainty of it from a mutinous crew. After all, it's best to have a happy ship, so far as it is possible.

So the sail was lowered, and Odysseus worked the ship round to the lee of the island, keeping his eyes skinned for a suitable spot for running in. He soon found it in a little bay of clean sand, well protected from the north and west by a bluff.

"All together now," he cried, more cheerfully than he really felt, "give way, men, and start her!"

The oarsmen pulled with a will, and for the moment at least their troubles were forgotten in the prospect of having the green earth under their feet and a comfortable supper. In a few minutes they were ashore.

As soon as the vessel was secured and everything stowed and shipshape, Odysseus called his men together and addressed them.

"My friends," he said, "we have been through many dangers together—and here we are, still alive and kicking. The gods love brave men, so let us keep our hearts up, and we'll be home in no time.

"But I have a caution for you. This island is full of fine cattle—listen! You can hear the lowing of the kine and the bleating of the sheep even from here. Well, don't touch them. You ask why not? Because there's a curse on them. They are sacred beasts, and whoever kills even one of them comes to a bad end. I have this on the most unimpeachable authority. So I beg you, my good men, to have sense and do as I

advise—keep off the cattle. It's not as if we were
short of provisions, as has so often been the case
before. We have plenty aboard. Content your-
selves with that—good meat and good wine—
and all will be well. But if you're fools enough
to disobey me, I don't answer for the consequences."

The men accepted what Odysseus said, for
they were perfectly willing to believe in the
curse; they had learnt many things in the
course of their travels far stranger than the
mere fact that certain cattle were taboo. So
Eurylochus, speaking for them, promised that
none of the animals should be molested. It was
an easy promise to make, for there seemed little prospect of any shortage of meat.

After this they all set about preparing an excellent meal from the stores they had on board,
ate it in comfort on the beach, and settled
down for the night in better spirits than for a
long while past.

Next morning it was blowing a gale from the
south. To put to sea was out of the question;
moreover, with the shift of wind the ship her-

self was in danger, and all hands had to set to at dawn to get the rollers under her keel and haul her right out of the water. That done, there was nothing for it but to wait for better weather.

The better weather didn't come. The southerly blow lasted for several days; then the wind flew into the east and blew harder than ever. They were pinned in the island as surely as the fleet at the beginning of the war had been pinned in Aulis.

These bad conditions lasted for a month, and by that time stores were running low. The men started fishing from the rocks to try to supplement their scanty rations. Spirits fell. A full stomach is the best heartener—and their stomachs were not full.

The mutterings began again.

Odysseus was anxious. He repeated his warning about the cattle, and once again Eurylochus, answering for his mates, promised to respect the taboo. Odysseus had to be content with the promise; but he knew hunger was an ill goad—and he didn't like it.

Then one day—in an evil hour—Odysseus, sick of the men's complaining and of their miserable and haggard looks, went off by himself inland in the hope that solitude might suggest to him some plan by which to escape from the island.

For hours he gave his best mind to the problem, but without success. No amount of thinking can stop the wind blowing. He even fell on his knees and prayed for guidance and help: there was no answer to his prayer.

Then he fell asleep.

Now this was the second time that Odysseus had fallen asleep at a crucial moment—the worse for him. But even an iron man must sleep sometimes; so we mustn't blame him.

When he woke up, he at once had a dreadful certainty that the worst had happened. He sprang to his feet and ran back toward the shore. Before he had covered a hundred yards, he smelt an unmistakable smell—the rich smell of roasting beef. That fool Eurylochus had broken his word.

Odysseus was white with anger when he con-

fronted him. Eurylochus met him with sullen
defiance. One by one Odysseus had up his
crew, charging each with deliberate disobedi-
ence. But what was the good? The cows were
dead, and no amount of indignation could
bring them to life again.

Hungrily and gloomily the men continued
to cook their nefarious supper, muttering that
any death was better than slow starvation, and
that they'd enjoy themselves while they could.

"And as for you, Odysseus," Eurylochus
said, "if you don't want to share our dinner,
keep away. Go and pick mussels off the rocks,
and much good may they do you."

A moment afterwards, however, even Eurylochus came near to repenting, for suddenly
they saw that the new-flayed hides were crawling with maggots, the slices of meat groaned on
the spits, and there was a sound like lowing
from the dead carcasses on the ground. This
was unpleasant; but hunger is a strong sauce,
and once the men had their teeth in the meat,
they ate till they were full.

For the next six days they stayed in the

in the wild water. Then every one of them was gone.

The wind flicked into the south, blowing great guns. Helpless on his raft, Odysseus was driven to the north and west, through the terrible Straits again, and out into the open sea beyond. Then the gale blew itself out, and for nine days without food or drink or sleep, Odysseus, astride his raft, drifted like flotsam over the sea and along the fishes' ways, until he was washed up on the island of Ogygia, the sole survivor of the five hundred who had set sail with him from Troy.

{ Odysseus Comes } to Scherie

No man in the world but Odysseus could have come alive through such a trial. It wasn't cunning or skill that saved him this time, but toughness of fiber, and a stout heart, and an invincible desire to live—yes, and luck too, or what we call luck in our ignorance of what it is that governs the destinies of men.

Of all the islands in the sea there is none more beautiful than the lost island of Ogygia. In it lived Calypso, an immortal being, always

126

lovely, always young, and always kind. She it was who took Odysseus in—a mere wraith of his former self, haggard, wasted, the spark almost gone—and clothed and fed him and nursed him back to strength.

Her house was hewn out of the rock and furnished with everything necessary for comfort and comeliness: polished chairs and settles, rich rugs, a loom with a golden shuttle, a wide hearth on which a fire of cedar logs was always burning. Outside to break the wind stood a grove of aspen trees and cypresses, where the sea birds roosted at night, and over the doorway trailed a vine heavy with grapes. Soft meadow grass with parsley and iris plentifully growing stretched beyond, watered by four clear streams. In a place like this it would be good for any man to live; for a shipwrecked seaman it was a paradise. The sweetness of it sank into Odysseus like sleep, and under Calypso's gentle hands he quickly grew strong again.

The days slipped by; the weeks, the months. The past—its dangers and exaltations, the ceaseless struggle with wind and water, monsters and men—was like a dream. Ithaca was very far away; his home—the bright cliffs, the haven, the fig tree on the wall, Penelope herself and Telemachus his son—all this was a story told to him long ago. Surely it was not he, but some other man, in a different life, who had felt that sudden irresistible fear that there in Ithaca all was not well, and that fierce desire to return. The fear, the desire were fading, like an old pain.

Lotus-land. . . . He smiled to himself when he remembered how angry he had been with poor Elpenor and Eurylochus for their wish to stay. Perhaps they were wiser than he after all.

This fairy isle was a far sweeter place than Lotus-land. Life is hard; few men are born to ease or to happiness, and if some beneficent fate offers them, surely only a fool says no.

And then, when such thoughts were in his mind, Calypso would come to him, and say: "Love me, Odysseus, and that will be your immortality."

Thus the months slipped into years, and

Odysseus was unconscious of their passing. To-day was like yesterday; both were a delight, and tomorrow the same sun would shine.

But the change came at last. It may be that as he stood on the beach, some gull flying out to sea at dawn seemed to him an image of his lost freedom; it may be simply that what a man is, that he remains—and if ever a man was born for deeds, Odysseus was he. But whatever the cause, the fact is that like an awakening the old restlessness returned; with it came a sudden shame for the years of idleness and ease, and a renewed certainty that the vision he had had in the Dark Land was not a dream but truth. His house was falling. . . . He, the master, was dead . . . somewhere on the sea bottom the bright fish were flickering between his ribs . . . he could never return. And Ithaca was full of evil men.

"Calypso," he said, "give me a ship. I am dying. Let me save myself, and save my house."

But there was no ship there.

"Give me a gull's wings or the fins of a fish, and I will go."

"Stay with me."

"I cannot."

"Love me, and live for ever."

"No."

Day after day now Odysseus would spend on the beach alone, staring out over the sea as he used to do when he was a boy in Ithaca; but not, as then, in longing to sail it for adventure's sake, but only to get home.

At last when the seventh year came round, he couldn't bear it any more.

"Calypso," he said, "you have been kind to me; I am not ungrateful. Look, there is timber in the island, cedar and fir and cypress. I will build my own boat and sail her home."

"I would not keep you against your will," Calypso answered. "*My* heart is not hard."

Then Odysseus took an axe and felled twenty trees, the best he could find, trimmed them up well and trued them with an adze, and sawed them into planks. Lucky for him he'd learnt the shipwright's craft in the yards of Ithaca long ago! The skill stood him in good stead now. Grimly he set to work, building his boat broad and strong, with a flat bottom and close-set ribs, decking her in, and putting bulwarks above of osier withies twisted close, backed with brushwood to protect him against spray. He made her a mast and yard, and cut a sail from cloth which Calypso herself had woven and gave him without a grudge. In four days the work was done. Calypso put aboard for him food and wine, the best she had, and water in a great skin, and rollers were got under the boat and she was run down into the calm sea. With a gay heart as of old, Odysseus climbed aboard.

"Stay with me," Calypso said. "Even now it is not too late."

Odysseus shook his head.

"There are more dangers waiting for you on the treacherous sea."

"I have faced them before and have not been afraid."

"Then good luck go with you."

Odysseus hoisted his sail. The warm wind filled it, and the little boat drew away from the land.

Night and day he sailed on over the lonely sea towards the East with the sun and the stars for company, until, after eighteen days, he came in sight of the misty hills in the country of the Phæacians.

Now the Phæacians, whose island was called Scherie, were a great seafaring people, so famous for the swiftness of their ships and their knowledge of the seas, that report had got about that they had magic power and a more than human skill. Coming thus within a stone's throw of their coast, Odysseus thought he was in luck, and that the last lap of his voyage home was more than half accomplished. Exhausted though he was by lack of sleep and the long days and nights at the helm, his spirits were high, and he was already looking forward to a comfortable bed that night and hospitable entertainment. The adventures and escapes he had had were running through his mind pleasantly enough, as is the way with perils passed; and he was congratulating himself in particular on the ruse by which he had got the better of the beast Polyphemus. Just at that moment, when he was chuckling with satisfaction at his own cleverness, the sea darkened under a puff of wind from the southward. The little boat heeled to it, almost putting her gunwale under, and Odysseus had a job to hold her. Then it fell calm again, and Odysseus was surprised to find that his throat was dry and the strength seemed to have gone from his knees.

How absurd! What was a puff of wind to him? His boat was a good one—and there was only another couple of miles to go. But the fact is, he had been scared.

What was it Eurylochus had said—if it was Eurylochus—after that business in the Cyclops' cave: that the God of the sea would punish him for the blinding of his son? Poseidon. . . . Try as he would, Odysseus couldn't get rid of the uncomfortable thought: there it was suddenly in his mind again, after all those years, pricking him.

His high spirits were gone. He felt nothing but an intolerable weariness. There was the land—so near: the green on the hills was already visible, and the friendly smoke. He longed passionately to be there; never before had he so hated the sea.

Then the squall hit him. The wind came off the land, screaming; then chopped into the south, veered west, and blew with the force of a hurricane. The mast went at the first shock. The helm was wrenched from Odysseus' hands, and a second later he was struggling in the water. He spat the brine from his mouth, grabbed at the boat's gunwale as a wave lifted her, and with a supreme effort hove himself aboard again.

The sea was getting up fast; the boat was a wreck; he had no means of controlling her— and he was on a lee shore. Unless the wind let up, he'd be smashed to pieces.

For a moment he thought of abandoning the boat and swimming for it; but what was the chance of living in such a sea as was running? He hung on—but not for long. Two minutes later he saw a great comber coming. Up it rushed with the speed of a race horse—nearer, higher—a wall of dark water, dreadfully hollowed on its inner side. For an instant it hung

right above him, then broke with a long, rever-
berating roar like a house falling down.

The next thing Odysseus knew was that he
was clinging, stunned and half-drowned, to a
fragment of wreckage—all that was left of the
boat. The rest had vanished.

But he wasn't dead yet. Once again the fierce
determination to live blazed up inside him. He
abandoned the plank he was grasping—it only
hampered him—and trusted to what strength
he had left to keep him afloat. The squall soon
passed, but there was still a confused and dangerous sea. That first blow off the land had
swept him back far from the island, and it was
impossible to judge how far he would have to
cover—when he could swim at all; for until the
sea went down he had all he could do merely
to keep afloat.

For two days and two nights the sea played
shuttlecock with him and tried to break his
heart—then it gave up, and the third morning
dawned as fair as paradise.

Odysseus struck out for the shore. A long
swell was still running, but the surface of the

sea was smooth as glass: not a ripple, not a breath of wind. As each swell lifted him, Odysseus looked anxiously to the land. It was very near.

Suddenly he heard breakers. The next swell, lifting him, showed him that the spot he was making for was all outlying reefs, steep-to cliffs,

and jagged rocks, on which the surf was pitilessly breaking. There wasn't a dog's chance of getting ashore there alive. Then, before he could think, he was right in the broken water.

A wave picked him up like a cork and swept him straight for the reef. He hit a rock with a whack that would have knocked any other man silly; but battered and bruised he got a grip and hung on. Then the backwash from the cliff got him, tore loose his grip, and swept him seaward again.

With the skin stripped off his hands and knees, and the breath pounded from his body, he made a desperate effort and swam clear of the broken water. Then he coasted along, paddling easily, in the hope of finding a possible landing place.

Presently the rugged cliffs were succeeded by gentle hills and smooth grassland coming down to the sea. Then to his joy, Odysseus saw a river's mouth. With renewed hope he swam for it, praying that he might reach it before his strength gave out. The water inshore was smooth; there were no rocks; but the current of the stream poured swiftly seaward. For a while Odysseus, almost spent, struggled against it without success; then by working his way close under the promontory at the mouth of the river, he found an eddy where the stream slackened. Once more he was able to advance, and at last, when he was at his last gasp, his feet touched bottom.

He crept ashore, hardly able to stand, his flesh swollen, his breath gone, water streaming from his mouth and nostrils—but alive. Once again he had defeated the malice of the sea. He dropped exhausted in the reeds, and kissed the earth in gratitude.

Then, when he had recovered strength enough to move, he climbed, all naked as he was, to a little hill above the bed of the stream, where there was a copse of trees. Here under thick-growing olives he made himself a nest of dry leaves, burrowed in, and fell asleep.

{ Nausicaä's Welcome }

THE ruler of the island of Scherie was Alcinoüs, and he had a daughter called Nausicaä.

Now the morning after Odysseus swam ashore, it came into Nausicaä's head, just as she woke up, that it was high time she had a grand wash of all the linen in the house. So as soon as she saw her father, she asked him for a wagon and mules, to load the linen in and take it down to the river at the point where it flowed into the sea—for that was the best place for washing: bright, running water, and stones hot with the sun, on which to spread the clean things to dry.

Alcinoüs was willing enough to let her have the wagon. Servants brought it along while the morning was still early, and piled in the linen and clothes. Then the girl climbed in herself, took the reins, touched the mules with the whip, and with a cheerful clatter jolted out of the courtyard of the fine house on to the track which led down to the river. Half a dozen of her maids followed on foot behind. There was plenty of food in the wagon (Nausicaä's mother had seen to that), and the girls, who were all young, intended when the washing was done to enjoy themselves and make a day of it.

Work first, however. All together they tossed the dirty clothes into the water where it ran shallow over the pebbles, trampled and kneaded them vigorously, rinsed them clean, and spread them out to dry on the shingle of the beach. Then they had a bathe themselves,

and immediately afterwards set to on the good
meal which Nausicaä's mother had provided.

The meal over, they began to play catch
with a ball which Nausicaä had brought; and
a charming sight they made—for they were all
pretty, though Nausicaä was by far the pret-
tiest. When they had played enough, they
folded the clothes, which by this time were dry,
and packed them back into the wagon. Then
Nausicaä, seeing the ball on the ground,
picked it up and tossed it to one of the other
girls, telling her to put that in the wagon too.
At least that is what Nausicaä intended; but
she threw it wide, and the girl missed it, and
it fell instead into the river. They all shrieked
with distress to see the colored ball go twirling
away down the stream.

Now only just above the riverbank was the
copse and the nest of leaves in which Odysseus
was curled up, fast asleep. He woke with a start,
the girls' shriek of distress still ringing in his
ears. It took him some moments to gather his
wits and remember where he was. He listened
intently—could it really have been girls' voices

he had heard? Perhaps, he thought, they were river nymphs, or spirits, or something of that sort—for his travels had accustomed him to expect surprises.

The best thing to do was to go and see. So, breaking off a branch to conceal his nakedness, Odysseus crawled out of the thicket. His eyes sunken and glaring, his hair and beard matted and tangled with salt water, his body white with the caked brine, he was not a pretty sight. All the six serving maids took one look at him and fled.

Nausicaä, however, mastered her fear and stood firm.

"Madam," Odysseus said, approaching her as politely as he could, "I ask only for your protection, and indeed I intend you no harm. Why! you are as beautiful as a young palm I once saw in the island of Delos; I have never seen a lovelier. I am in great trouble. Only yesterday I escaped from the sea, after nineteen days of terrible hardships, and you are the first human being I have met. Will you show me the way to the town, and give me some rag to

cover myself with? I am sure you are kind, and heaven will reward you with what you most want—a good husband, perhaps, and a happy home."

Nausicaä was much relieved by Odysseus' courteous words.

"Stranger," she said, "you will certainly not lack clothes or anything else we can provide. I will show you the town with pleasure and tell you who we are besides. We are Phæacians. Our ruler is Alcinoüs, and I am his daughter."

"Girls!" she went on, raising her voice; "what are you running away for? Just because you've seen a man? Come back at once. He's been shipwrecked, and we must help him. He must have something to eat and drink—and a bath too."

The girls came gingerly back, each pushing another in front of her, hardly knowing if they were still scared, or if the whole thing might not be a great joke after all. They were a little ashamed of themselves too, and did their best to take their cue from their mistress, who they saw was perfectly serious and not at all frightened.

"Come now," Nausicaä went on, "you must wash the salt off him, and let him have some oil to rub himself with, and some of the clean clothes—the best you can find. Don't stand there like idiots."

Odysseus, however, took the matter into his own hands.

"I do indeed want a bath," he said, "but I

should much prefer it if you all went a little farther away, so that I can get on with it privately. The oil, and something to wear, will be a real luxury."

So the girls and their mistress withdrew, and Odysseus had his bath in the fresh water of the stream, rubbed himself afterwards with the olive oil till his back and shoulders gleamed, and put on the clean clothes. You wouldn't have known him for the difference it made. Nausicaä, when she saw him again, was astonished at how fine and handsome he looked.

"I hope," she whispered to her maids, "that this stranger will decide to stay here. Why, he's just the sort of man I've always thought of for a husband!"

After that, Odysseus was given a meal; for there was still plenty left in the wagon. He was as hungry as a lion, and no food had ever tasted better.

Then they started for the town. Nausicaä told Odysseus to follow behind the wagon with the maids until they reached the outskirts of the town; then he was to wait in a field, until he thought she would have had time to reach her father's house. It wouldn't do, she said, for the people to see her coming along with such a handsome stranger—they would undoubtedly talk. But once she was safely home, Odysseus could follow by himself: anybody would tell him the way.

"And when you come in," Nausicaä ended, "go straight up to my mother and ask her protection. She's sure to give it to you; and once you have my mother on your side, you'll be all right."

Nausicaä touched her mules with the whip, and off they clattered. Odysseus and the girls followed behind.

Odysseus obeyed all his instructions to the letter; indeed, he wouldn't for the world have caused Nausicaä distress after her generous welcome. He waited in the field until he was quite sure she would have had plenty of time to get home; then he walked on toward the town. It was near sunset, and a misty evening —which was lucky, for the fewer people who saw him the better. There were rough characters amongst the seafaring population, and they might not have been pleased at the sight of a stranger.

He passed the stone causeway, and couldn't forbear to stop a moment in the growing dusk to admire the ships which lay along it. His practiced eye told him at once that they were splendid vessels, built and designed by master craftsmen: real fliers. Hardly anyone seemed to be about, and Odysseus was just beginning to wonder how he would find his way to Alcinoüs' house, when he saw a young girl coming toward him along the street by the water front.

Another girl! Seldom had Odysseus had such an agreeable reception in a foreign place before. The girl smiled in the friendliest way as she came up, almost as if she had expected him, though, of course, she was a perfect stranger. It seemed like a providential meeting.

"My dear," Odysseus said, "could you tell me where to find Alcinoüs' house?"

"Of course I can," the girl replied; "in fact I will take you to it."

They set off together, past a great temple

on the edge of the harbor, and through several well-paved streets, the girl telling Odysseus on the way a number of things about the previous rulers of the island, and about the people, too, and their marvelous skill in seamanship. As they walked, several people passed them, but for some reason appeared to take no notice of the pair. This struck Odysseus as odd, especially after what Nausicaä had said about meeting loiterers. It wasn't dark yet—only dusk; and the people must surely have seen them; moreover, it could not have been a common thing to see an obviously well-bred young woman escorting a foreigner through the town so late in the evening. But there was something still odder to come; for when they reached the door of Alcinoüs' house, and Odysseus turned to thank his companion for her kindly help—she wasn't there! She had vanished.

Well, wonders will never cease. Odysseus used to say in afterdays that it must have been Athene herself in disguise—for he always believed that the goddess Athene was his particular friend, and helped him out of his worst scrapes. Perhaps he was right.

In any case, there he was at Alcinoüs' door, which stood wide open, as the door of a hospitable man should.

Odysseus was used to fine houses, for he had seen plenty in the course of his travels; but he had never seen any so fine as the house of Alcinoüs. It outdid even the palace of Tyndareus in splendour. Two great watchdogs guarded the entrance, and it wasn't till you had safely passed them that you realized they were made of silver, so lifelike they looked. The banquet hall had bronze walls which threw out a wonderful soft radiance of their own, and further light was given by torches held in the hands of golden figures set on pedestals. There were no fewer than fifty maidservants in the place.

The garden was as fine as the house, and even more beautiful. There was not only a vegetable garden, elaborately laid out and watered by two clear streams, but also an orchard of fig, pomegranate, and pear trees perpetually green, some blossoming, others setting their fruit, others ripening it, so that at all seasons, even in winter, enough and to spare could be gathered—so blessed was the climate of the island.

Supper was in full swing when Odysseus arrived, and a large company was assembled, as was usual in the house of this hospitable prince. Odysseus marched up the banquet hall and, remembering Nausicaä's advice, went straight to where Arete, Alcinoüs' wife, was sitting by the fire, on a carved chair with a high back, spread with a richly colored woven coverlet.

Without hesitation he flung himself at her feet and put his arms round her knees, as suppliants do.

"Lady," he cried—and all the guests at supper stopped talking and stared—"I beg help for a shipwrecked sailor! Out of your goodness, and the goodness of your people, lend me a ship to take me home."

Having made his petition, he sat humbly

down on the ground by the fire, amongst the ashes.

Alcinoüs saw at once that Odysseus was no common beggar. He took his hand, made him get up, and offered him a chair. Then he ordered a servant to bring him food and a bowl of wine. Odysseus ate and drank with an excellent appetite—for a man, as he himself remarked, can't help being hungry, however unfortunate his plight. It was quite obvious that he had made a good impression not only on Arete and Alcinoüs, but also on the company in general; for he had scarcely finished his supper before the guests at table, in answer to Alcinoüs' inquiry, heartily voted their readiness to sail him home—wherever that might be—on the very next day.

The guests departed, and Odysseus was left alone with Arete and Alcinoüs. Now Arete had been looking with some curiosity at Odysseus ever since he had come in, not only because he was such a fine figure of a man, but also because of the clothes he was wearing. She had seen those clothes before.

As soon as they were alone, therefore, she went straight to the point without further ado.

"Who are you, sir?" she said, "and where did you get those clothes from?"

Odysseus was never a man to give everything away at once, so he didn't actually say who he was. He did, however, explain about the clothes, with a few details added about the terrible time he had had on his passage from Ogygia.

Alcinoüs listened with deep attention to his account of the storm. He was a seaman himself, and appreciated such things. Then, when Odysseus finished, he said: "That daughter of mine behaved well enough--but I do think she might have brought you home, instead of leaving you to come by yourself."

"She was perfectly right," Odysseus answered. "I admire her modesty. Moreover, it occurred to me too that you might not like our driving through the town together."

"Nonsense," said Alcinoüs, "I see at once that you are a man after my own heart. I trust you entirely. Indeed, I should be only too happy if you would settle amongst us. But no doubt you want to get home, and heaven forbid I should stop you. We'll arrange your passage as soon as you please—tomorrow if you like. And I venture to believe that even you will be surprised at our seamanship."

This was very satisfactory, and just what Odysseus wanted.

It was now getting late; a bed was made up for Odysseus, and he was soon drowsing into sleep.

Tomorrow he would start for home—tomorrow. It seemed incredible. How long was it he had been away? Nearly twenty years! What would he find when he got home? Those premonitions of evil that had pressed upon him, and pressed still—were they empty dreams, or truth? And if they were true, would he still be in time to save what he loved?

{ The Stranger } { in the Palace }

Next morning Alcinoüs held a council of the leading men of the island, because he wanted to tell them his wishes about making arrangements for shipping Odysseus home. Everybody hurried to the meeting, being filled with curiosity to see more of their remarkable visitor and to find out who he was.

"So get a vessel ready for sea at once," Alcinoüs said, when he had declared his purpose. "Let her be the finest ship of the fleet, and man her with fifty-two picked men. After that there will be an entertainment at my house for everyone who wants to come, including the crew. And don't forget to bring Demodocus with you; for we shall want some stories while we are drinking our wine."

The orders were promptly obeyed, and before noon the guests were assembled in Alcinoüs' house. They had a splendid meal; and as soon as they had eaten enough and were warmed with wine, Demodocus the blind minstrel was asked for a tale. What was Odysseus' astonishment when almost the first word the minstrel spoke was his own name! Odysseus, son of Laertes, the Ready-at-Need, the Sacker of Cities . . . his own name, with all his titles complete!

It was like a finger laid on his heart.

Demodocus went on to tell a tale of the war at Troy, how Odysseus and Achilles had quarreled. So the fame of those days had spread across the world—and his own name more than all! There were tears in Odysseus' eyes as he listened. To hide them he drew his cloak over his face.

The guests at table were too intent upon the tale to notice how deeply Odysseus was moved; but Alcinoüs saw, for he was sitting close at his side. Wondering, perhaps guessing, what the reason might be, and wishing like a good host to spare his visitor distress, he at once put an end to Demodocus' tale.

"Come," he said, "enough of eating and drinking and storytelling. Let us take the field and show our guest something of our prowess in sports, running and wrestling and boxing and jumping, and anything else besides."

The young men of the company were eager enough to do as Alcinoüs suggested. So out they went, and were soon followed by most of the population of the island—thousands of them—to the place of assembly; for nothing attracts a crowd like a sports meeting.

The games began. They made a fine spectacle, and the crowd roared and cheered with as much enthusiasm as can be. As for Odysseus, he sat quietly with Alcinoüs; sports are all very well—but he had more serious things to think of just then.

While he was sitting thus, watching the races with an abstracted eye, two young men, Laodamas, one of Alcinoüs' sons, and Euryalus came up to him.

"Sir," Laodamas said, "why don't you take a hand yourself in something? From the look of you—if you will pardon my saying so—you should be no mean athlete. Enter for a race; or perhaps throwing the discus is your favorite event."

Odysseus shook his head. "I have too much on my mind," he answered, "to think of that sort of thing now."

Euryalus didn't like this answer. He glanced at his friend, and then said with a sneer: "Leave the old fellow alone, Laodamas. Obviously he's not up to it. He's only an old shellback after all. Sports are for gentlemen."

Odysseus' eyes blazed with anger.

"Sir," he said, "it isn't looks that make a gentleman, or perhaps you might be one yourself. But I see you're a fool. You have insulted me."

With that he sprang up and seized a disc—a huge stone one, much bigger than what is generally used. Without even taking his cloak off he swung and hurled it. It whizzed through the air with such alarming speed that everybody who was anywhere near instinctively ducked to avoid it; then it crashed to the ground a tremendous distance beyond all the other throws.

Odysseus smiled to himself with evident satisfaction.

"Beat that, if you can," he said. "You've put me on my mettle, and I'm quite willing to show you a thing or two in boxing as well, or wrestling—anything you like. Come on— any of you—if you've got the courage."

Euryalus hadn't a word to say. He could only stand biting his lips and looking foolish at his mistake. Moreover, nobody else came forward to accept the challenge; that terrific throw of the disc had taken the heart out of them.

It was an awkward moment, and Alcinoüs himself had to intervene to put things right again.

"Sir," he said to Odysseus, "I apologize for this man's rudeness, and hope you will forgive it. It was no way to treat a guest. We will stop the games at once, and, if you are willing, I will order a display of dancing. It will please you, I believe—our dancers are said to be the best in the world."

Odysseus gladly consented to see the performance, which did, indeed, surpass his expectations, especially the Catch-Ball dance, which was given with wonderful grace and agility by two young men, to the music of the lyre and the rhythmical stamping of the spectators around the edge of the ring.

"Your dancers," he said to Alcinoüs, "are indeed the best in the world. They fill me with wonder."

These generous words of Odysseus, added to the pleasure which all had felt in watching the dances, put the company at ease again; and presently Alcinoüs, after giving his final instructions to the ship's crew to have everything ready for putting to sea at dawn on the following day, once more invited the most distinguished of his subjects to supper.

"And each one of you," he added, "will, I am sure, show your respect and friendliness toward our guest by bringing him as costly a present as you can afford. I shall not myself allow him to leave us empty-handed: of that you may be assured."

They left the level field and made their way to the great house. Soon after, the other guests arrived bringing their presents, which were very fine and rich. Euryalus made up for his rudeness by giving a splendid bronze sword with a silver hilt and an ivory scabbard, and Alcinoüs himself gave a drinking cup of beaten gold. Arete ordered a big bronze chest to be brought out, and into it she packed the presents with her own hands, adding for her own a woven mantle and a tunic of the best linen. When the packing was done, Odysseus lashed up the chest with rope, finishing with a special knot which he said Circe had taught him—nobody could possibly undo it but himself.

Then Arete told the servant maids to heat water in a cauldron for Odysseus' bath, an exquisite pleasure to him after his hardships on the sea. When it was done, and he had rubbed his body with olive oil and put on the new clothes which Arete had provided, he both looked and felt taller and stronger and handsomer than ever.

With a light step he went into the hall where supper was prepared. The long room was already crowded. Close to a pillar by the fire stood Nausicaä. She was the first to see him as he entered, and for a moment their eyes met.

"Friend," she said, as soon as he was by her side, "may good fortune always be yours—and when you are home again, I hope you will not forget me."

"Princess," Odysseus answered, "I shall think of you as of a goddess all the rest of my life. For it was you who saved me."

No other words were spoken between them, and the banquet began.

When everyone had eaten to his heart's desire and the wine was going merrily round, the minstrel Demodocus was summoned for another tale.

"No minstrel has a sweeter voice than yours," Odysseus cried, "and you tell the tale of the Greeks at Troy so well that you might have been there yourself. Come now—I beg you to continue the story. Tell us of the famous stratagem of the Wooden Horse, for I cannot think that it is unknown to you."

The tale was not, indeed, unknown to the blind minstrel; and as soon as Odysseus had spoken, he began. With thrilling words, touching the strings of his lyre, he unfolded the story; and Odysseus, as those far-off days of danger and endurance lived for him anew in the minstrel's song, once more felt the finger laid upon his heart. Tears came. He hid his face in his mantle and wept like a woman for sorrow and pride at all that was past, and for the strangeness of hearing his own name familiar on this man's lips.

No one but Alcinoüs saw his distress, for Demodocus' lay held all the company spellbound. But Alcinoüs saw, and touched Odys-

seus lightly on the arm—and wondered. Then he called for silence.

"My friends," he said, "there is one amongst us who weeps at our minstrel's story. Tales are for mirth and pleasure, so let us make an end."

Then he turned to Odysseus.

"Sir," he said, "a hospitable host asks no question until his guest has received all that he needs for his help and comfort. But the time has come when I must beg you to answer me.

"Who are you, sir? What is your name and country? For indeed, I cannot send you home unless I know in what land you live. And why do you weep when you hear the story of Troy?"

Odysseus uncovered his face and raised his head. All eyes were upon him. In the long hall there was not a sound.

When he spoke, his words were grave and quiet.

"How should I not weep? For Odysseus, son of Laertes, prince of Ithaca—that man, my lord, am I."

For an instant there was silence again. Then a sound like a sigh ran through the hall, and a moment later a hubbub of voices broke out, and a great stamping of feet and scraping of chairs on the floor, as each man exclaimed to his neighbor at this astonishing news, and tried to get a better view of the famous fighter and seaman who had come so unexpectedly amongst them.

Once again Alcinoüs called for silence.

"My friends," he cried, "all strangers and guests are from God. We little knew that the one we are entertaining now had sent his fame before him into the farthest corners of the world. Come: we will hear his story from his own lips."

A smile, like the beginning of pleasure after pain, hovered on Odysseus' mouth. He was not unwilling to do as Alcinoüs asked; so after the briefest pause he began. All his adventures by land and sea, from the war at Troy to his coming shipwrecked and naked to Scherie, just as you have already heard them, he related to the assembled company; and before he had finished, the stars were growing pale and dawn was not far away.

The Home-Coming

JUST BEFORE THE sun rose they
were aboard the ship, but not yet were they
put to sea. Odysseus was impatient to be
gone, but the captain of the ship shook his
head.

"We sail," he said, "only when night is on
the sea. That is our law. Many strangers we
have taken to their homes between dusk and
dawn—while they were sleeping."

Odysseus declared that on such a voyage as

this he wouldn't sleep a wink. The idea was preposterous.

"*I* sleep?" he exclaimed. "*I* close my eyes, when all they long for is the sight of the cliffs of Ithaca? You deceive yourself, my friend."

But the captain only smiled.

"That's as may be," he said. "We sail at sunset."

Odysseus had to be content; but the long day made weary waiting. All the presents which he had received were carefully stowed aboard, under the thwarts, together with an ample provision of food and wine, all of the best; and when that was done, and the ship was ready for sea, Odysseus once again returned with Alcinoüs to his house. Alcinoüs did his best to entertain him; but in spite of music and banqueting and talk, and all the arts of hospitality which that generous prince could practice, the hours went by with leaden pace, and all that Odysseus could think of was of how far the slow sun had traveled on his journey toward the west.

But at last the day was done. Torches were

lit in the house, and the sunset colors glowed
in the sky. Alcinoüs rose from his chair and
for the last time took his guest by the hand.

"May the gods go with you," he said.

"Heaven prosper you also," Odysseus answered; "and keep all harm for ever from your
hospitable land."

Then with a squire to accompany him
Odysseus stepped out into the gathering dusk.

Through the wide gardens, and down the
cobbled street of the little town they walked
to where, alongside the quay, the vessel was
moored. Her head lay toward the east. The
quayside was deserted; there was no sound of
human life. The ship's crew sat upon the
thwarts or stood ready by the halliards without a word. Then, at the very moment
that Odysseus stepped aboard, the sun's rim
touched the sea, and a wind came strong and
sweet and kindly from the west. Odysseus
glanced at the captain questioningly; but the
captain did not meet his eyes. His arm lay
across the steering oar, and he gave no sign.
On the deck, by the captain's feet, a rug was

spread, rich, thick, and soft, and over it a sheet of white linen. Wondering at himself, and treading softly, Odysseus went to it, as if he were walking in a dream, and the ship, and the ship's silent company, did not belong to this world.

He lay down, unbidden. Suddenly the fear which had first touched him in the Land of Ghosts—the fear and foreknowledge of danger and death which were threatening his home— rushed back on him. He struggled to rise, to cry *Quick! Quick!* to that silent and mysterious crew; but the words faded on his lips. He sank back, and a heaviness as sweet as it was strange took possession of him. For an instant, it seemed, he was aware of stars in the pale sky, and of the ship moving with an urgent and impetuous speed such as no ship had ever equaled. Then darkness.

I wish I could tell you of that voyage, for the Lord knows it was a queer one. But I cannot; I know no more about it than Odysseus did. That ship had magic in her. How far was it from Scherie to Ithaca? Fifty miles—or a hundred? Nobody knows; but this I do know, that even if it had been a thousand, it was all one to those Phæacian seamen: they would have done it in a night between dusk and dawn, while Odysseus slept.

When Odysseus woke, he found himself on the beach and the ship gone. Daylight was beginning to grow. He looked round him, wondering and half-afraid, for there was a mist on the water and lapping like another tide round the base of the hills, and he could see nothing but spectral cliffs and the shadowy sea. It may be there was mist in his eyes too; for not yet, indeed, had he fully awakened from his dream. All was strange—lonely and silent as the beginning of the world.

He struggled to his feet, fingering the hilt of his sword, turning his head this way and that, trying to pierce the mist, and listening. Suddenly he saw a great score in the sand by the edge of the sea, as if a ship had beached there and had leapt, with the rush of her speed, half her length on to the land. And there, where he had lain, was the rug with the linen sheet over it, and, piled close by, the tripods and cauldrons and weapons of bronze which the men of Scherie had given him—and the great coffer fastened with the knot he had himself tied.

A surge of bitterness swept over him. So—they were traitors after all, these men who had seemed so kind! They had brought him to some unknown island, and marooned him there to mock him!

The mist thickened, and with heavy steps Odysseus set off along the margin of the sea.

He had not walked far when he became aware that he was not alone. He stopped; and when the crunch of his feet on the stones was stilled, he could hear another tread, nimble and light, and very near. Then a whistle and a snatch of song; and a moment later he saw through the mist the figure of a young man swiftly approaching him. The young man—he was hardly more than a boy—was dressed like a shepherd.

In a minute they met.

The lad was of extraordinary beauty and as

gay as morning. Odysseus dropped to his knees and stretched out his arms in the attitude of a suppliant.

"Sir," he said, and felt no strangeness in thus addressing a shepherd boy, "by all the gods who care for the unfortunate, I adjure you to tell me—what country is this?"

The boy laughed. "You must have come from a long way off, my friend," he said, "or else be mighty ignorant not to know this island. Why, the fame of Ithaca is all over the world!"

Odysseus could not speak.

"Don't you believe me? Come; we'll climb this path together, and you'll soon know I tell no lies."

Odysseus followed where the boy led, still feeling that he was walking in a dream; but, as he ascended the rugged cliff, he was aware of a warmth growing about his heart, and suddenly, as he reached the top, the mist cleared.

For a full minute he stood as still as a stone —staring. Then, with a sob of wonder and gratitude and love, he threw himself down

and pressed his face into the turf, as a lost child who has been found again presses his face into his mother's lap. He was at home.

When he got up, the boy was gone.

The mist had indeed vanished, not only from the cliffs but from Odysseus' eyes as well. He was entirely himself again. Eagerly he looked about him: away to his left was the wooded promontory of Neriton; below, the

little harbor which he had loved from boyhood, with its rocky horns and the stream
splashing down; to his right the roofs of the
village where the shipwrights lived; and all
around, the steep cliffs falling to the sea. In
front, beyond the rounded hill, was his own
house: he could see the smoke from it above
the tops of the trees. Yes, he was at home: all
was as it had been, twenty years ago.

But . . . was it? Suddenly his fear came back.
Hills don't change in twenty years, nor cliffs,
nor the sea, nor houses—much. But what of
Penelope? And of Telemachus his son?

The impulse seized him to run to his house
with all the speed he could, burst in on them,
and cry: "I have come home!" But, partly in
caution, partly for dread of what he might
find, he crushed the impulse down.

Suddenly he remembered the shepherd
boy, whom his excitement had for the moment quite driven out his head. But now
his face and bearing, and his mocking but
friendly laughter, returned to his mind with
startling vividness.

"*He* could have told me," he muttered, angry at himself for being so foolish. "I should have asked him . . . how they were . . . if all was well. . . ."

But it was too late for that. The boy was no longer in sight. Not that he could be very far away, Odysseus thought, unless he had wings: it was only two minutes since they had been talking together. He ran back to the top of the cliff path, and called. There was no answer—at least, he was pretty sure that what he heard was only the echo of his own voice.

Odysseus was vexed—and puzzled. He was vexed because he wanted much more than he could see any reason for to see the young shepherd again, and he was puzzled because of a growing feeling that his face was familiar. But how could that be? The boy was not even born, not by many years, when Odysseus was last in Ithaca. Yet—he had seen him before.

He was just about to shout again, on the chance of making the boy hear, when he checked himself, and listened. That whistle . . . it might have been a bird; or it might not. He listened again, intently, straining his senses to catch a repetition of the sound. Then, quite suddenly and without his knowing why, his tension relaxed, and he smiled, and nodded his head three times as if in assent.

"Of course," he said to himself, "*that* is what I should do."

Indeed, his course of action was now perfectly clear to him. I can't say that he had thought it out, for he hadn't yet thought at all. The short time since he had found himself in Ithaca had been too full of strangeness for thinking. The knowledge—the knowledge of what he must do next—was simply there, in his mind, almost as if he had *heard* it instead of that clear whistle he was hoping for.

Eumæus! He must find Eumæus. If anyone in Ithaca had the interest of his house at heart, it was the old swineherd. He was the loyalest of servants—and he'd have all the news. From him, Odysseus could learn precisely how things stood in the island, whether the fears which continually haunted him were justified or groundless; and, if justified, he could lay his plans and count on the old man's help to carry them out.

In spite of his anxiety Odysseus was almost happy again. At last he could act. Ever since he had stepped aboard the Phæacian ship there had been a spell on him. But now it was broken, and he was once more his own man. With a light step he returned to the beach where his gear was lying and, with all his old caution and common sense, stacked the precious things which his former hosts had given him in a cave near the water's edge, lest anyone passing that way might see them and rob him. And all the time that he was busy about this task, he was thinking.

Twenty years! It was a long time, indeed, for the master to be away. Without doubt everybody in the island must think him dead, Eumæus amongst them. It wouldn't do to present himself too suddenly even to Eumæus. He must proceed carefully, cunningly. It might well be that after so many years Eumæus would not recognize him at once; but on the other hand he might—and Odysseus would take no chances.

He smiled to himself as he stripped off the fine clothes which Arete had given him. Next he lit a fire of driftwood at the mouth of the cave, took his mantle and, after slashing it in tatters with his knife, blackened and singed it in the heat and smoke until it was a shapeless and colorless rag. Then he rubbed his face and hair and beard with dirt from the floor of the cave, picked up a long, gnarled stick, and, stooping almost double, hobbled off with a limp along the edge of the sea, chuckling as he went. If anyone looked like a tramp, Odysseus did in his disguise. Not Penelope herself would have known him.

Then he climbed the cliff path again, and made the best of his way to the swineherd's cottage.

⟨ The Faithful
Eumæus ⟩

IT DIDN'T TAKE Odysseus long to
follow the remembered track through woods
and over hills to the place called Raven's Rock
where Eumæus' cottage stood. The cottage
was set high on an eminence, close to the pig-
sties, in a good, spacious yard walled round
with a stone wall.

The dogs flew at him as he entered by the
gate, but they were soon called off by their
master, who was sitting by his cottage door

busy with a pair of sandals which he was cutting for himself from a strip of leather. Seeing
Odysseus, however, he at once got up and
came toward him. One of the dogs, with his
hackles up, was still growling near his feet.

"Well, old fellow," he said, "they might
have torn you to pieces if I hadn't stopped
them. They're savage. Get away, you brute!"
and he tossed a stone at the growler.

"But come into my hut, my good man. You
shall have a meal and anything else you want,
and then you can tell me your troubles.
You've had plenty, by the look of you."

While Eumæus was speaking, Odysseus had
been watching him narrowly under his eye-
lids. Now, in spite of his own woebegone and
dilapidated appearance, he could not repress a
smile. His disguise was satisfactory: there was
no doubt about that. As for Eumæus, twenty
years had not changed him much: he was not
quite so nimble on his feet, perhaps, and the
leather of his skin was a little tougher and
drier than it used to be; but—and this was the
important thing—he had the same kindly

heart as ever, and a glance at him had been enough to convince Odysseus that he was still a faithful and loyal servant on whom he could depend. Nevertheless, he must proceed cautiously and get all the information from him that he could.

Eumæus led the way into the cottage, made Odysseus sit down on a pile of heath with a fleece on top, and at once set about preparing some food for the poor beggarman. As Odys-

seus watched him, the face of the gay young
shepherd flashed back into his mind. He was
on the point of asking Eumæus who the boy
was, when he suddenly remembered where he
had seen his face before. That girl—the girl
who had met him in the street and taken him
to Alcinoüs' door—had had just such a look;
and she had just as suddenly, just as mysteri-
ously, gone, before he could speak more
words. But she was a girl, this was a boy. . . .
Well, no matter; a seaman becomes used to
wonders. The face was the same: Odysseus
had no doubt of it; and—what was the strangest
of all—the recollection of it was like a renewal
of strength to him, and a promise that, whatever it might be of evil that he was to hear
from Eumæus' lips, he would yet win through.
He had a mighty helper. That boy . . . that
girl. . . . Well, well—the gods don't appear to
men in their proper shapes. Men couldn't
stand it if they did. They disguised themselves. But there was no doubt about it—not
a shadow: Athene herself, his divine protec-

tress, had once more shown that she would not desert him in a time of trouble.

Eumæus, like all men who live much alone, was eager to talk when he was lucky enough to have a listener; and Odysseus did not have long to wait before he learned that he had come home not a moment too soon. Sitting on his fleece, he watched the old man shaking his head and grumbling to himself as he cut up the meat for their meal, and every now and then glancing up at his guest, as if to say that they would have plenty to tell one another once their tongues were loosened.

Presently the swineherd began. Thrusting the spit through a strip of pig meat, "There now," he said, "poor men like us must make do with what we have and be grateful. It's rough fare, old fellow, but you're welcome to share it, such as it is. And it's not only the fare either. No indeed. Times are not what they used to be in the old days . . ." and he let out a sigh which told Odysseus that his mouth was as full of news as his own would soon be of roast pork. However, he paused and began shaking his head again in a melancholy fashion, to give a relish to what was coming.

"Yet you have a snug cottage," Odysseus said, "and a fine herd of pigs, and a well-kept farm. Your master is a man of consequence, I don't doubt. Come now—things are not so bad, by the look of them."

"What the eye doesn't see, the heart won't grieve over," the swineherd answered. "The cottage is good enough, and the pigs, and the farm. And so they should be, for my master was the best man in all the islands."

"Was? Why—is he dead?"

"He's drowned. For nineteen years I waited for him, and kept my hope. But I shall never see him now. The fishes have eaten him. And the old master is out of his wits, and the young one—still hoping, poor lad—is away looking for news. But he won't get any. Twenty years is a great space of time, and it's best to take what heaven sends and not grumble. The master's dead and done for—and up at his house yonder there's a pack of thieves plundering his property and eating the mistress out of house and home."

When Odysseus heard this he could hardly refrain from leaping to his feet and declaring himself. Good sense, however, got the better of impulse. He bit his lip and waited for Eumæus to go on.

"Yes—worse than thieves. A thief's an honest man compared with them. A thief trusts to his wits and stakes his life; and if he loses, why, that's the end of him. But this pack—that call themselves gentlemen! But what is my poor mistress to do, alone as she is, and the young master away? And even were he here, what's one against so many? My mistress is a fine lady, and rich, and not so old either, and it's not to be wondered at that these precious gallants seek her hand; but that's no cause for them to turn her house into an inn for their gluttony and drunkenness. Not a day but they send to the farm for their hogs, a couple of the best, and a half-dozen of sheep for the table. And who's to stop them? See here now—I honor a woman for loyalty to her husband, living or dead; but it would be best, to my thinking, if my mistress took one of them and made an end of it. It's foolishness to hope when the grounds of hope are gone."

All the time the swineherd had been speaking, anger was boiling up in Odysseus, and with it a great thankfulness that his wife and his son were still alive, and that he was in time to save them, if only he could find a plan.

"Tell me," he said quietly, "who is your master?"

"Why," the swineherd answered, in a tone of surprise, as if all the world should know anything so obvious, "Odysseus, of course, son of Laertes, Sacker of Cities, and Lord of Ithaca. He *was* my master."

Odysseus leaned forward and touched Eumæus on the knee.

"My friend," he said quietly, "don't be so sure that Odysseus is done for."

The swineherd's only answer was a shake of the head and a sigh.

"Now listen to me," Odysseus went on. "Like a good host you've asked me no questions until you saw to my needs. But now I'll tell you something. I'm a traveled man; I've seen the world—before ill luck got me. I've not always been a beggar—not by any means. I've known good company in my time, and not so long ago either. I am a native of Crete, and had my estate there like any other gentleman. But I won't tell you all my troubles—I'll come to the point. It's this: you've heard tell of Pheidon, maybe, who is a great man in the country of Thesprotia—No? Well, he was a friend of mine, and only a month ago I was in his house, living on the fat of the land like a lord—and *he told me Odysseus was alive.* He'd had certain news of him: not a doubt about it. There now, my friend! You've started your mourning before the funeral. Cheer up; that master of yours will be home before you know it—and won't he make mince-meat of those fellows who are playing the deuce with his property!"

The swineherd was not to be convinced. He continued to shake his grizzled old head even when Odysseus added that, from information which he could not doubt, his master was actually on his way home, and would land in Ithaca at any moment.

"You can't catch an old bird with lime," he said. "I've heard too many such tales. I believed them once—but never again. My master is dead."

The day wore on toward evening. In the course of their talk Odysseus learned all he could of the state of things at home: how his dream in the land of ghosts had been true, and Anticleia his mother was dead; and as for Laertes, how grief for his lost son had bewildered him and he did nothing but potter amongst his herbs, dressed in rags like a common laborer, his former wealth and pride quite forgotten. But Penelope was true, and Telemachus, it seemed, had grown tall and strong and brave, and was just the son he had always wished to have.

And all the time as they talked, Odysseus' rage against the pack of scoundrels who were taking their pleasure in his house grew hotter, and he was turning over in his mind the ways by which he might get even with them.

Toward sundown the four herdsmen who worked under Eumæus came in from the fields with their beasts, and supper was prepared. A fat hog was killed, singed, and cut up, Eumæus not forgetting to put aside a portion as an offering to his Gods; and when the meat was well roasted over the fire on spits, the six men fell to and regaled themselves, washing down the savory meat with wine, of which Eumæus still kept a good store.

Darkness came on; and as the night grew, the wind got up, cold from the north, with a fine rain. The herdsmen piled wood on the fire till the little room was as hot as an oven, and then went to their quarters to sleep. Odysseus and his host continued talking by the cheerful blaze until dawn was only a few hours away; then the swineherd made for Odysseus a bed of thick fleeces spread on brushwood with a warm mantle over all, and Odysseus lay down, tired after the long day, but with his head still full of many thoughts.

As for Eumæus, he wrapped himself up in a cloak, took a weapon in his hand, and went out to sleep in the open where his boars were penned, to make sure that no harm came to them from robbers in the night. Odysseus smiled to himself when he saw him go, well pleased that he still had so good and faithful a servant.

{ Odysseus and His Son }

Odysseus' son telemachus, sick of his failure to hear any news of his lost father, and fearing that the state of things at home would become even worse if he prolonged his absence, said goodbye to Menelaus, at whose house he had been staying in Sparta, and made his way overland to the western coast of Greece. As luck would have it, he reached the port of Pylos, where his ship was lying, on the very evening which Odysseus was spending in the swineherd's cottage. He went on board and at once put to sea, sailed through the night in fine weather with a fresh south-easterly breeze, and landed in Ithaca on the following morning.

Hard times and the presence in his house of the rascally suitors had sharpened young Telemachus' wits, until he was almost as wary a tactician as his father. He didn't bring his vessel into the harbor, but landed on the coast in a concealed and sheltered spot, to avoid trouble; for he had a shrewd suspicion that some of the gang would be on the lookout for him to do him a mischief. Safely ashore, he thought it would be the best plan not to go straight to the house—where, indeed, he was far from welcome these days—but first to seek information about whether or not the position there had deteriorated during his absence. The obvious person to consult was the faithful swineherd; so, just as his father had done, he made his way with all speed to the cottage under Raven's Rock.

Odysseus and the swineherd were having a

bite of breakfast when they heard the gate click. Both looked up, listening.

"That's no stranger," Odysseus said. "The dogs don't bark."

A moment later Eumæus was out in the yard. Through the open door Odysseus saw him fling his arms round the young man's neck and kiss him in joy, and heard him greet him by his name. Then the two turned and crossed the yard to the cottage.

They entered, and Odysseus, still sitting by the freshly kindled fire, looked at his son.

"Why, who's your guest, uncle?" Telemachus said. "He looks comfortable. Trust you to give a welcome to anyone!"

His arm was about the swineherd's shoulder, and he spoke gaily. Odysseus, watching him, felt the tears in his eyes—it was like looking at his own youth.

"He comes from Crete, dear boy," Eumæus answered. "He's down on his luck, poor fellow."

Telemachus sighed. "I'd entertain him at home with pleasure," he said, "if I were master in my own house. Guests and beggars are from God, eh, uncle? But he'd get short shrift there now. That pack of devils would be the end of him. You must keep him to yourself for a bit."

Eumæus replied that he was willing enough; and when Telemachus had asked him a few questions about the state of affairs at home, he said he would be much obliged if he would go up to the house and take the news to Penelope of his safe return.

"And mind," he added, "don't let anyone else know I've come."

Eumæus gladly obeyed, and Odysseus was left alone with his son.

For a minute neither of them spoke. Odysseus was troubled by the presence of this tall young stranger, who was yet so close to him and so dear, and by the knowledge that the moment of recognition was soon to come. Presently he rose to his feet and, bent double and leaning on his staff in his beggar's guise, shuffled to the door and out into the yard. He felt his heart beat quick. He hurried to a trough of clear water which stood in a corner of the yard, plunged in his arms up to the elbows, washed the dirt from his face and hair and beard, then drew himself up to his full height, flung away his stick with a laugh, and strode back to the cottage.

At the sight of him Telemachus stared wide-eyed in astonishment and admiration.

"Unless I'm wandering in my wits," he said, "it was a bent old beggar who left me just now. But you, sir—you might be one of the gods."

"No god, Telemachus, but Odysseus, your father."

The blood left the young man's cheeks, and he trembled, afraid to believe what yet his heart told him was true.

"My father is dead," he muttered.

"For nineteen years he was near death, but he is home again. Telemachus . . . my son!"

A moment later they were in each other's arms, both weeping for joy at their reunion.

But there was not much time for tears, the need for action was too pressing.

"Tell me," Odysseus said, "is it true that these scoundrels are in our house?"

"It is indeed," Telemachus answered. "And if they are there much longer, there won't be any house left. They're eating us up like locusts."

"And your mother?"

"She is true to you. But what can she do? All believe that you are dead, and they press her to choose one of them. But she will not. She delays and delays. Every day she weaves at her loom, and gives it out that when the weaving is done she will make her choice—and every night she undoes the work of the day. As for them, they make free with our property and live like lords. The house is a mere tavern."

"How many are there?"

"More than a hundred, with a crowd of servants besides."

"I'll tear the heart out of every one of them!"

"Father, take care! What can the two of us do against so many?"

"Boy," Odysseus cried, "the gods themselves will fight on our side! Now listen to me, for I've already got a plan ready. Trust me for that! Enter the house tomorrow and let these fellows see you—that won't please them, if you're right in thinking they were plotting your death. You'll be safe enough: they won't dare attack you openly. I'll come along later, in my beggar's disguise. I'll beg their alms, as humble as you please; and whatever they do to me, mind you don't turn a hair—not even if they throw things at me or drag me out into the yard by my foot. Swallow your anger: it will make our revenge the sweeter." .

"All the time you must watch me; for when the moment comes—I'll know it, never fear!— I'll give you a nod. That will be your signal. The instant you see it, gather up all the weapons that are lying about in the hall, or propped against the pillars, or hanging on the walls, and carry them off and lock them up in the strong-room. If anyone asks you why you're doing it, invent some yarn—say they've been there too long and the smoke is spoiling them

—anything that comes into your head. They'll be mellow with drink in any case; and even if they were sober they'd never suspect what's coming to them. And leave a couple of good spears and a couple of swords for ourselves— we'll get our hands on them right enough when the time comes. You understand?"

Telemachus nodded.

"And mind you don't tell a single soul—not even your mother—that I'm home. You'll ruin everything if you do. Swear it."

"No need of an oath, Father."

Odysseus smiled. The light of battle was in Telemachus' eyes already, and the sight of it was enough to convince Odysseus that he need not fear. He could have no better ally than his son.

The farm gate clicked again. Odysseus glanced sharply up. It was the swineherd, back from his errand to Penelope. Odysseus slipped silently through a back door of the room into the yard, leaving Telemachus alone. When he returned a few minutes later, he had recovered his stick, smeared his face and hair with dirt, as before, and hobbled along bent double, like the poor beggar that Eumæus believed him to be. Telemachus avoided meeting his eyes.

That night the three remained in the cottage, and early next morning Telemachus went off to the house to show himself to the suitors and to greet his mother. The suitors, who had indeed been plotting his death by an ambush to catch his ship in the straits, were full of rage to see that their treacherous plan had failed. But they had to make the best of it, and wait for another chance; for to attack him openly would have aroused the anger of the island and perhaps brought vengeance upon them. Meanwhile they were compelled to treat him courteously, as master of the house, meeting him with smiles on their lips and murder in their hearts.

Later in the day the swineherd, according to instructions which Telemachus had given him the previous evening, set off with Odysseus toward the town. Just where the rough track topped the rise before descending to the plain, they met a man driving some goats.

Though twenty years had not improved his
looks, Odysseus quickly recognized him. It was
the goatherd Melanthius, swarthier and more
bandy-legged than ever.

It was soon apparent that the twenty years
had not improved his manners either.

"Ho, ho!" he said. "Here's a pair to meet on
a fine morning! Birds of a feather, eh? I never
saw two dirtier scoundrels."

The path was narrow, and as Odysseus
passed, the goatherd landed a kick on his thigh.

Odysseus bit his lip.

"Trying your luck at the big house, eh?"
Melanthius called after him as he walked on.
"It's not work you want, that's plain. You want
a free meal."

The two men, the beggar and the swineherd,
passed through the streets of the little town,
and began to climb the hill beyond, on the
southern slope of which the great house stood.
To Odysseus, as he hobbled along beside his
companion, every stone, every tree, every curve
and hollow of the hills was full of memories,
and as close to him as the beating of his blood.

He felt a sudden exaltation, a fierce joy; for all his troubles he was a lucky man. How many hundreds—how many thousands—had left their bones on the plains of Troy? Poor ghosts! But he had lived: he had seen sights of beauty and strangeness and terror such as no man before him had ever seen. Life had been sweet; and now his vengeance on his enemies would be sweetest of all.

They entered the court of the house, and approached the great door. In a corner of the court a dog was lying. Hardly knowing why, Odysseus went to him. He was very old and feeble, his shaggy coat matted into lumps from neglect. He had been a fine beast once, but all his beauty was gone.

The dog raised his head and, not deceived by the rags and the staff and the shuffling steps, looked at his master with loving and liquid eyes.

"Argus!" Odysseus whispered.

The dog would have answered if he could; but he was too weak. There was nothing left for him but death; but he had seen his master again, after so many years, and died content.

Odysseus felt the tears in his eyes, but rubbed them angrily away and rejoined Eumæus by the door of the house. A moment later they went in.

As soon as the door was opened they were greeted by a sound of music and laughter and gay voices and clinking dishes, for the suitors were at table. They entered the long hall, and Odysseus sat humbly down, as beggars do, on the floor just inside the threshold, while Eumæus made straight for his young master Telemachus and asked him for meat to take to the poor beggar. Odysseus received it and put it away in the wallet which he carried; then, wishing to take a closer look at his enemies, he got up from the ground and went round the tables, begging from each of the young lords in turn, stretching out his left hand for alms as if he had done it all his life. From many of them he got a crust or a slice of meat, until he came to where Antinoüs was sitting.

As he stretched out his hand Odysseus

looked at Antinoüs: a long, hard look, under his brows. It was the same Antinoüs he had played with as a boy, but never loved, and beaten in contests with the bow.

"A crust for the beggar, kind sir!"

"Get away from my table," Antinoüs replied with an expression of disgust. "The sight of your dirt spoils my dinner."

"Kind sir, indeed!" Odysseus boldly answered. "I see now you're not the sort of man to give away a crust—even when it doesn't belong to you."

Antinoüs in a rage picked up a stool and flung it. It struck Odysseus on the shoulder—but he didn't flinch. He stood in silence, shaking his head. Then he went back to his place by the door, and Telemachus was forced to watch him, and could do nothing to protect his father from insult.

Meanwhile Penelope, who was in her room upstairs, heard of the beggar's arrival from the housekeeper Eurynome, and of the inhospitable way Antinoüs had treated him. She sent for the swineherd and asked him who the beggar was. Eumæus replied—what indeed he thought was true—that he was a Cretan, and went on to tell his mistress of the beggar's claim to have had news of Odysseus.

"Ah!" said Penelope, "if only his tale were true! If only my husband would return, and punish these men for their crimes!"

At that moment Telemachus sneezed: a great loud sneeze which could be heard all over the house above the noise and clatter of the suitors at their meal. Penelope, sad though she was, couldn't keep back a laugh.

"An omen!" she cried. "My son has sneezed a blessing on my prayer! All may yet be well."

She was anxious at once to see the beggar and to hear his story from his own mouth; but when the swineherd brought her message to Odysseus, he was unwilling to come until the late evening, when the suitors would have gone back to their homes for the night.

The feast in the great hall went merrily on. The sun went down and torches were lit. The minstrel sang; dancers entertained the company; stewards bustled round filling cups which a minute later were again empty; faces grew more flushed, voices louder, and manners worse.

Presently another beggar made his appearance in the hall, a huge, burly man, as fat as an ox and very dirty. His name was Irus, and for many months he had been a hanger-on of the house, and had made an excellent living out of it, being willing to go errands for the suitors, or do any other easy task in exchange for food to fill his carcase.

This fellow was annoyed to see a rival sitting by the door.

"Make way for your betters," he growled. "Unless you want to be thrown out."

"There's room for both of us," Odysseus answered. "You'll get bloody teeth yourself, unless you're careful."

"Spoiling for a fight, eh?" Irus blustered. "Off with your coat then, if you've got the pluck."

Antinoüs, who was not too drunk to notice what was going on, was highly delighted with this turn of affairs.

"Here's luck!" he cried. "Free entertainment for us all! Come on, my friends, we'll give a prize to the winner—and no foul play."

Meanwhile Odysseus had got to his feet, bared his powerful chest and tucked up his ragged cloak, revealing his muscular thighs. The sight was a surprise to all the company, but especially to Irus, who at once wished he had been more polite. He turned pale and began to shake like a jelly. Indeed, he would have backed out of the fight altogether, if Antinoüs, afraid of being robbed of his fun, hadn't roared that he'd have him packed off to the ogre Echetus to have his nose slit, if he shirked.

So Irus was dragged into the ring. Up went their hands, and Irus aimed a blow at Odysseus' head. Lightly Odysseus brushed it aside, and with utmost ease and deliberation hit his opponent just below the ear; and such was the weight of his fist that the bones cracked under it, the teeth were loosened, the mouth filled with blood, and Irus, all the sense knocked out of him, measured his length on the floor.

Odysseus took him by the foot, hauled him

into the yard, propped him up against the wall, and told him to beg elsewhere in the future. Then he resumed his seat within the threshold of the hall.

The suitors were much pleased with Odysseus' prowess—Antinoüs sent him a titbit from

his own table; and another, Amphinomus by name, amidst the general congratulations, came close and pledged him in a cup of wine, and wished him better fortune.

"Ah," said Odysseus when he had drunk, "a man's luck is a slippery thing. Up one day and down the next. Look at all these fine fellows now—fortune's darlings, living high on another man's property! Well, well, it's my belief that the real master of this house is not far away. When he comes home—let them look to it."

Amphinomus made no reply. He went back to his friends and tried to smile; but Odysseus' words had filled him with foreboding.

Odysseus
and Penelope

LATE THAT EVENING, when the unwelcome guests, unable to eat another mouthful or drink another drop, having talked, laughed, sung, and quarreled to their hearts' content, went back to their several homes to sleep, Odysseus and his son, according to their plan, collected the weapons which stood or hung in the banqueting hall and carried them upstairs into the storeroom, taking care to leave only enough for their own use when the time should come.

Hardly was this done, and Telemachus gone to his bed, when Penelope, unable any longer to restrain her curiosity about this beggar who claimed to have news of her lost husband, came down into the hall and took her seat on a chair close to the fire.

The servants were still up, and Eurynome the housekeeper was keeping an eye on them as they cleared away the fragments of the suitors' supper, hurrying from table to table in the quivering light of the fire and the torches. Presently Penelope called the beggar to come to her, and made him sit down on a settle by her side. The servants looked more than they dared to say at this mark of favor to a ragged vagrant, but Penelope, though she was aware of their glances, paid no attention. She at once addressed Odysseus.

"Sir," she said with queenly courtesy, "I will be bold, and ask you your name without further ado."

"Lady," Odysseus answered, "the fame of

your goodness has spread over the world; and
for that very reason I beg you to ask me any
question but that, and I will tell you no lies."

"Alas, sir," Penelope said, "if I had merit
once, it all vanished away when my husband
sailed from Troy. Now I have nothing left but
sorrow and shame. Odysseus is dead. You have
seen these men who seek my hand—mere beasts
who devour all that is mine and my son's. For
three years I have put them off with pretences;
but now my parents say I must delay no
longer, and there is no escape for me.

"But tell me your story, sir. Indeed and indeed I must hear it."

Had the hall been empty save for Penelope
and himself, Odysseus might then and there
have revealed the truth. But it was not yet safe.
So with a sigh he told her a lying tale, as he had
told the swineherd. But this time he mixed his
tale with matter so like the truth that Penelope's heart swelled and she began to hope,
though she knew that hope was vain.

"For there in Crete," Odysseus said, "I welcomed your husband once into my house and

entertained him, when he was bound for Troy. Listen—he was wearing a purple cloak, doubled, with a golden brooch; and on the brooch, for a device, was graven a hound tearing a fawn."

Hearing of the cloak, which she herself had made, and of the brooch, which had been her own gift, Penelope burst into tears.

"That was twenty years ago," Odysseus continued. "But dry your eyes: you haven't heard the end yet. Was Odysseus killed at Troy? Not he. He is alive, and I've had news of him. The crew of his ship were drowned at sea, but he escaped. At this moment he is in Thesprotia, and he will soon be home. Lady, I tell you the truth. This very year—no, this very month, before the new moon—he will return."

Penelope longed to believe; and, whether what he said was true or false, her heart was softened toward the poor beggarman.

"Sir," she said, "you shall be my guest indeed tonight." And with that she called to the maidservants to make a bath ready for Odysseus and wash his feet, and bring a clean mantle and tunic to put on instead of his rags.

The bath was quickly prepared; but while the water was heating in the bronze cauldron, a thought occurred to Odysseus which made him knit his brows.

"Madam," he said to Penelope, "my vagrant life has made me unused to luxuries like this; and believe me—I would never let any of these saucy girls of yours attend to my bath: not even to wash my feet. But if there should happen to be in your service some staid old woman with a kind heart who will not mock at a poor tramp like me I should not object to her washing my feet."

Penelope replied that she had indeed just such a servant, and immediately sent for her.

It was none other than the old nurse, Eurycleia.

One glance at her, and Odysseus looked away, though he dearly wished to press her hand against his cheek. The glance was enough to tell him that the old woman's body was almost worn out in its long and humble service of love, but that the spirit was alive and looking through her old eyes which were still bright.

"And what a to-do is this, my lady," Eurycleia began almost before she had reached the door, "with yourself sitting half the night with tramps and beggars, when you should be in your bed? A proper scarecrow he is—yet he's seen better days, take my word for it. If he wants a bath, sure it's myself should give it him. There's too little kindness in our house, since the master went away, for the like of me to grudge it to anyone, tramp or no tramp.

"Come then, my dear, to where the bath is set, at the end of the hall yonder."

"Eurycleia," said Penelope, "yours is a good heart. The poor man is just of your master's age; and who knows—if indeed he lives—whether Odysseus himself is not come to such a pass?"

Odysseus and the nurse went to the end of the long hall, leaving Penelope on her chair by the fire, and with gentle hands Eurycleia began to wash Odysseus' feet.

While she was washing them, the rags of his
tunic fell open, and on his thigh the old woman
saw the scar which long ago the boar's tusk had
made. She put her hand on it and looked wildly

in Odysseus' face, and dropped his foot, which
struck the edge of the bath with a clang and
overturned it so that the water was spilled.

"My master," she gasped, "Odysseus. . . ."

But Odysseus caught her by the throat, and
with his other hand pulled her to him.

"Hold your tongue," he hissed. "Do you want to ruin me? Nobody must know . . . not one. Betray my secret and I'll kill you with the other traitors."

"Master . . . dear master . . . I'll be dumb as a stone."

Then she dried Odysseus' feet tenderly, and tears of joy poured down her cheeks.

When she was gone, with not another word spoken, Odysseus rejoined Penelope, who had neither seen nor heard anything of what had passed.

"Friend," Penelope said, "it is time for sleep; but I cannot sleep. Talk with me a little longer; there is comfort in talk for one who has grief like mine. I had a dream last night: an eagle swooped down from the hills amongst my geese, broke the necks of every one with his beak, and then soared away out of sight. What did it mean?"

"It meant that, like the eagle, Odysseus will return, and break the necks of his enemies."

Penelope sighed. "If only it were true!" she

said. "But I fear my dream came through the Ivory Gate, like the other false ones. Bear with me, my friend, and let me tell you another thing: the hateful day is near when I must leave this house and take another husband. To-morrow I must make my choice—and this is how I will choose: Odysseus, my dear lord, had a bow which he left in my care when he went to fight against the accursed city of Troy. It is a weapon of terrible power. This bow I mean to put into the hands of my suitors, and which-ever of them is strong enough to string it, and skillful enough to shoot an arrow through the curved heads of twelve axes set in a row, that one I will take for my husband, and go with him from this house which I love and will al-ways remember, even in my dreams."

"Good luck to the contest!" Odysseus an-swered. "And I will tell you a thing myself, lady: Odysseus will be home before any of those fine fellows can string his bow, or shoot an arrow to its mark."

Penelope shook her head. "I could talk with you till dawn," she said. "But there is a time for sleep, even for the unhappy. I will go to my room, where every night I have wept since my husband went away. And as for you, sleep here, if you will, by the fire—or let the servants make you a bed."

She left him; and the torches in the hall burnt out, the fire flickered low, and Odysseus, wrapped in a rug and mantle, lay alone, turning over in his mind what the next day might bring.

{ The Fight } { in the Hall }

It happened that the next day was the feast of the god Apollo, to be marked with a banquet of unusual richness and splendor. Early in the morning the herdsmen brought their beasts to the house, to furnish the meat; Eumæus his hogs. Philœtius his sheep, and black Melanthius his goats. The maidservants were busy from dawn sweeping the hall, preparing the tables and rekindling

219

the fire, under the sharp eyes of the house-keeper and Eurycleia.

When the bustle in the house awoke Odysseus from his uneasy sleep, his first thoughts were gloomy ones; for it was indeed an unequal battle that he would have to fight. A prayer to Zeus, king of the gods, formed itself on his lips; and hardly was it uttered when a peal of thunder crashed down from the hills, as if in answer, and one of the maidservants dropped her pail with a clatter and exclaimed: "An omen! Thunder from a clear sky! Somebody's in luck, I'll be bound. If it was me now, and I had my wish, this would be the last time that ever I swept a floor for these new masters. May they get what they deserve!"

Odysseus was cheered by this. It was a lucky sign, and he was soon his confident self again.

Meanwhile Telemachus was up, and, after asking Eurycleia if she had attended properly to the poor vagrant, had gone off with his dogs into the town; for it was wiser, he thought, to have no communication with his father just yet, in case the secret might get out.

Hearing the noise of the herdsmen and their beasts in the courtyard, Odysseus went to join them. Eumæus greeted him with a cheerful word, but Melanthius the goatherd soon broke in on their talk.

"So we haven't seen the last of *you* yet," he sneered. "I rather think you'll feel the weight of my fist before much longer, if you don't take yourself off."

Odysseus made no answer. He shook his head and bit his lips into silence.

Then Philœtius gave him a good-humored nod, wished him good morning, and asked his name.

"I can see at a glance," he said, "that you've had bad luck. But you're welcome, so far as I'm concerned. Would you believe it now—you put me in mind of our old master, the good Odysseus himself. Ah well! They say he's dead and gone, and more's the pity. Yet the gods play queer tricks on us: maybe he's alive yet, and I for one still hope for the day which will see him home again, and sending these rascals about their business."

"Would you help him fight for his own—if he did come?" said Odysseus, watching him.

"Ay, that I would. He could have the last drop of my blood—for what it's worth. He was a good man, and a good master."

Odysseus was glad when he heard this speech, because it told him that here was another of his servants who was true, and that when the battle began he and his son would have two friends at least to fight on their side.

By noon the preparations for the banquet were complete, and the suitors, who had passed the morning trying to devise another plot for the murder of Telemachus, came crowding with much noise and laughter to the house, all intent upon a day of unusual merrymaking and extravagance, such as fitted a celebration in honor of Apollo, God of the Bow.

When they had taken their places at the long tables, and the stewards—servants of their own, young men with curled and scented hair, and delicately dressed to please fastidious eyes —were busily serving the wine and bringing the bread in baskets and the platters of roast meat; and when, the libations made to the Archer God, heads had already begun to grow heated and tongues to wag, and each princeling present thought himself better than the rest and the chosen suitor of Penelope: then it was that Odysseus came back into the hall and sat down as before in the dust within the threshold of the door.

Telemachus, seeing him resume his humble seat, approached him courteously and put for him a stool to sit on and a table for his food.

"This is no tavern," he said, "but Odysseus' house—now mine, for I am his son. And I ask the company to treat you with proper respect."

He looked proudly round as he said this, and the suitors, unused to such bold words from Telemachus, were indignant, and Antinoüs muttered that if he had had his way they would never have been spoken—or any others either.

And now a certain Ctesippus, a wealthy and insolent person who had come from the neighboring island of Same to try his luck with the rest, called out that he had a way of dealing with beggars, which would prove as effective as any.

Knowing their man, the others laughed, and Ctesippus, shouting out that the beggar, though he had food on his plate already, could no doubt do with some more, picked up the hoof of an ox from the dish where it was lying, and hurled it at Odysseus' head.

Odysseus avoided the missile by a quick movement, and it struck the wall behind him with a thwack.

Telemachus' eyes blazed with anger, and despite himself his hand went out to one of the spears which he and his father had left ready for their use. But he caught Odysseus' eye, and was forced to desist. His gesture, however, and his look of rage did not pass unnoticed by the turbulent company. For a moment they were silent; then somebody laughed—then another; and presently the hall was filled with peals of wild and helpless laughter. It rang under the rafters like madness, and all the while Odysseus sat silent on his stool, looking at the ground.

Suddenly the laughter died. There was a hush, as if some spirit had come amongst them and touched them with cold fingers. Faces grew pale, and it seemed to each that the meat in front of him was dripping with blood.

"Woe to the wicked!" cried a voice. "There is darkness round you, and a wailing. Blood is on the walls, and the house is filled with ghosts. See! They are hurrying to that place from which there is no returning."

A shiver passed through everyone present like wind through corn; but an instant afterwards Antinoüs snatched his cup and lifted it, and cried: "Come, my friends, what ails you? We'll have no spoilsport at the feast. Drink and be merry."

The wine was poured, the blood came back to blanched cheeks, and soon the drunken hubbub was as wild as before. The evil moment, it seemed, had passed.

And now Penelope, who in her room above-stairs had been all the while listening with a chill foreboding to the uproar in the banqueting hall, went with a heavy heart to the storeroom to fetch Odysseus' bow. She wept as she took it up, for the sight of it brought to her with a new poignancy the memory of her husband. But she steeled herself and went with it in her hands down to the hall.

The uproar subsided when Penelope appeared, and she stood for a moment without speaking by one of the columns that supported the roof, and drew her headdress half across her face. Then she said: "My lords, listen to me: for a long time now you have wasted my wealth and my son's, under the pretense of seeking my hand, knowing that my husband is dead. I propose a challenge to you. Here is my husband's bow; whoever of you can string it, and shoot an arrow through twelve axe-heads to the mark, shall take me for his wife."

The suitors muttered to one another uneasily. It was a formidable bow; and though each hoped secretly that he might succeed in stringing it, yet they all doubted their strength. Telemachus laughed at the sight of their glum faces, and told them gleefully to come forward and contend for the prize—a lady who had no equal in all the islands, or in Greece itself. He flung off his cloak and made a trench in the earthen floor of the hall, and set up the twelve axes in a line, and stamped them in hard and firm; then he seized the bow, and tested his strength with foot and hand to string it. It quivered under the pressure, and the string was nearly over the notch, when he saw Odysseus shake his head. At once he desisted, and heaving a pretended sigh he laid the bow on the ground, saying he was too weak and too young for such a task, and must leave it to his betters.

The next to take it up was Leodes, an elegant young man, but not born to be a bowman. He very soon found that the task was beyond his strength.

"This bow will be the death of us," he said. "Not a man here will string it."

Antinoüs turned on him in anger at such ill-omened words.

"You are a fool, Leodes," he said. "Give *me* the bow."

Antinoüs, however, had no intention of try-

ing his luck yet. Confident that he was the best
man present, with the exception of his friend
Eurymachus, he preferred to see others try first
—and fail. So he told a servant to fetch tallow
from the store, that they might grease the bow
and warm it at the fire to render it supple.

When the servant had come back with the
tallow and was greasing the bow, Odysseus got
up from his stool and stepped quietly out into
the courtyard, where he knew he would find
the cowman Philœtius and Eumæus the swineherd, his two trusty men.

"Now listen," he said, speaking low, "if
Odysseus were here, would you fight for him?"

"To the last breath," said Philœtius.

"Would to God he were here indeed," said
Eumæus, "that I might show him!"

It was no time to waste words; so Odysseus
said at once, "Well, my trusty men, he *is* here.
I am he. Look . . ." and he pulled aside his
ragged tunic and revealed the scar on his thigh.

For an instant the two servants stared, unable to believe their eyes. Then with a gasp

they flung their arms round their master's neck
and kissed him.

"Quick now," Odysseus said, "I'll tell you
what you must do. Follow me into the hall—
first one, then the other. I shall ask for the bow;
and you, Eumæus, make sure I get it. Tell the
women to keep to their rooms—with the doors
locked. You, Philœtius, see the gate into the
courtyard is bolted."

The men nodded, and Odysseus went
quickly back into the hall and resumed his seat
on the stool. The two servants followed, at in-
tervals of half a minute.

Eurymachus now had the bow, and after a
preliminary try was warming it a little more at
the fire. Then, grasping it firmly and bracing
the lower horn against his foot, he exerted all
his strength—but in vain.

"The cursed thing will make us look like
fools," he muttered, and flung it on the ground.

Antinoüs smiled, pleased at his friend's failure; but before making his own attempt, he
called for more wine to improve his spirits.
But when the cup was empty, Odysseus antici-

pated him, and in a humble voice called out from where he sat by the door: "Kind gentlemen, my lords, let *me*, poor tramp though I am, handle the bow. I was a strong man once—but no doubt my miserable life has sapped my strength."

Antinoüs burst out in a rage. "You? You dirty rascal? Isn't it enough for you to share our dinner? You're drunk—that's what's the matter with you. Hold your tongue, or we'll soon have you off to the ogre to get your nose slit!"

"Preposterous!" exclaimed Eurymachus. "I suppose he thinks *he* has a chance of marrying the queen."

At this Penelope could hardly help smiling in spite of her distress. "Certainly not," she said. "But should he succeed in stringing the bow, I'd give him some new clothes and see him safe to wherever it is he wants to go."

"Mother," said Telemachus, "the bow is *my* concern. I shall do as I please with my father's property. I am master now."

At this rebuke Penelope returned to her

room in the upper part of the house and locked the door, and Telemachus, turning to the swineherd, ordered him to carry the bow to Odysseus.

The suitors were very angry, and abused him so heartily as he passed down the long hall that Eumæus dropped the bow and stood still in indecision. Telemachus, however, ordered him sharply to take it up again, repeating what he had said to his mother—that there was only one master in the house.

Eumæus obeyed; and a moment later the bow was in Odysseus' hands. That done, the swineherd made haste to carry out Odysseus' other order, and having sought out the nurse Eurycleia instructed her to keep all the women of the house out of the way behind locked doors. Then he sat down, and kept his eyes on Odysseus.

For a full minute Odysseus turned the bow about in his hands to test and examine it, while the young lords watched him, half in anger, half in contempt. Then, with no more effort

than a man needs to string a lyre, he quietly
and without haste strung the bow.

The suitors turned pale. Odysseus plucked
the bowstring to test it, and it gave out a soft
and mellow twang which seemed to fill the hall.
Immediately after, there was a clap of thunder,
and Odysseus' heart leapt at the omen of success.

Then, as quietly as before, he fitted an arrow
to the string, and, without rising from his
stool, took aim and let it fly. Through the
twelve axe-heads the arrow sped unerringly to
its mark.

"Your guest," said Odysseus, turning to his
son, "has brought you no shame. Come now,
let us see that the banquet ends as banquets
should, with music and dancing."

With that, he nodded his head; and Telemachus, in obedience to the sign, snatched up
a sword and a spear and took his stand by his
father's side.

Suddenly as by a flash of lightning the beggar's disguise fell from Odysseus. He sprang to

his feet, as terrible as a lion and bright with the glory of battle, the bow in his hand and a second arrow on the string.

"That game is played," he cried; "and now I have another mark!"

The great bow bent; the arrow leapt, and Antinoüs, the wine cup in his hand, fell backward to the ground pierced through the throat.

"You dogs!" Odysseus cried again. "Know me at last for who I am—the master of this house, who you thought would never return.

Look your last upon each other and upon me;
for your doom is sealed."

So swift and unexpected had the attack been
that the suitors were paralyzed with fear. The
blood drained from their cheeks, and their
knees shook. For a minute they could only
stare stupidly at their dead companion with
the arrow in his throat.

It was Eurymachus who rallied them.

"Draw your swords," he shouted, "and at
them!" And without waiting to see if he was
followed he made straight for Odysseus. But
he hadn't taken two steps before another arrow
sped. He dropped his sword, and fell sideways
across the table with a crash amongst the food
and the wine—and darkness covered his eyes.

Amphinomus next plucked up courage to
attack, but Telemachus killed him with a
spear-thrust from behind before Odysseus
could shoot. The others still hung back, each
hoping that his neighbor and not he would be
the next mark for the deadly bow.

"Father," said Telemachus, "we must arm

Eumæus and Philœtius before your arrows are spent."

Odysseus nodded; and Telemachus made his way swiftly and secretly to the armory, and in a minute was back again with spears and shields. Thus armed the swineherd and Philœtius took their stand by Odysseus' side. And all the time, slowly and deliberately, Odysseus kept shooting with his bow; and with each shot another man went down to his death.

Presently there was a stir amongst the suitors, huddled at the farther end of the hall, and a moment later they were putting on breastplates and helmets, and a glitter of fresh swords could be seen in their hands. Odysseus saw the goatherd Melanthius slip away through a little door leading to a gallery by which the armory could be reached. Following the direction of his eyes, Telemachus saw him too.

"I left the door of the armory unlocked," he whispered. "After him, Eumæus—catch him before he can bring more."

Eumæus and Philœtius both slipped away; and almost as soon as they were gone, Odysseus

shot the last arrow in his quiver. He laid his
bow on the ground and grasped a spear.

It was a black moment. Seeing that the arrows were spent, their enemies were getting
courage to attack. Forward and back they
surged, with threatening shouts and gleaming
spears—still many against two. But before they
could make their rush, Philœtius and the
swineherd were back, their errand done and
the treacherous goatherd caught and killed.

"Now for it—sword to sword, and spear to
spear!" cried Odysseus.

With the courage of desperation the suitors
charged and a volley of missiles was hurled at
Odysseus and his three companions. But Odysseus' luck was in, and not one found its mark:
instead, four more of the enemy bit the dust of
the floor.

Then Odysseus shouted his battle cry, and
the four men advanced upon their foes. Terror
again struck the suitors dumb; for at the sound
of that cry a strange light seemed to flicker and
burn amongst the rafters of the roof, and the
pillars of the hall were edged with fire, and

Odysseus himself seemed to have grown to a terrible stature and irresistible strength. The hall was filled with the clash and clatter of sword on shield and helmet, the strong gasping of men, shrieks, and cries strangled in the throat by the gush of blood.

Then all was over. Only the minstrel Phemius was spared and allowed to creep from the house, where the bodies of those to whom he once sang lay sprawled and twisted across chairs and tables amongst the remnants of their meal, or heaped on the ground in fantastic images of death.

Odysseus sent for the old nurse, who all the while, with the other servants behind locked doors, had been listening to the din below with a beating heart. When she came into the hall, her eyes grew wide with mingled horror and glee; she fell on her knees before her master, and kissed his hands; but of all the words in her mouth, not one could find a way out. For once Eurycleia was dumb.

"Go to your mistress, and tell her that the house is purged of the plague that was consuming it; for Odysseus, her husband, has come home."

The old woman hobbled away on her joyful errand, chuckling through her tears; and a few minutes later Odysseus himself followed her to Penelope's room.

{ The Last Scene }

A HEART which for many years has been possessed by sorrow, does not lightly believe in the return of joy.

When Odysseus entered her room, Penelope remained sitting in her chair, looking downward, and did not speak.

"Do you not know your husband?" Odysseus said.

"Sir," Penelope answered, "if you have killed those wicked men, you are a warrior indeed, and not the poor wanderer who asked my charity. But it is cruel to deceive me now; for my beloved husband will never return."

As she said this she looked for a second in Odysseus' eyes, and something in her leapt.

"Dear nurse," she went on, turning to Eurycleia, "make a bed for our guest. Move out the big bed—my husband's own. He must sleep soft tonight."

Again as she spoke she glanced at Odysseus under her lashes. Her heart beat hard.

"Move the big bed?" Odysseus exclaimed. "Why, that's impossible—unless some rascal has been playing tricks while I was away. I built that bed with my own hands, Penelope, when I brought you home as my wife. And I built the bedroom too, round the olive tree which grew in the courtyard. What a trunk that olive had! I cut the branches off, and smoothed it all the way up so that it shone like a pillar. And that was our bedpost. Tell me now—who could move a bed like that, without cutting down the tree? And *that* you would never have allowed. And when I had fitted the bed to the post, I inlaid the wood with ivory and silver and gold. Penelope—it was our own secret!"

When Penelope heard this description of their bed, exact in every detail, her knees

trembled. She could doubt no longer. She rose from her chair, flung her arms round Odysseus' neck and kissed him.

"Forgive me," she whispered through her tears. "You are indeed Odysseus, my beloved husband."

Once again that night Odysseus told the tale of his adventures, and Penelope listened, lying in the crook of his arm with her head on his breast. It was a long and happy night, for Athene herself, it is said, delayed for them the coming of the dawn.

On the following day nothing was left for Odysseus but to make his old father Laertes happy too, by the news of his return. He found him in the herb garden hoeing his plants and dressed in rags. Wandering as the old man was in his wits, it was no easy task to make him believe that what he had desired for so many years had at last come to pass. But when Odysseus had shown him the scar on his thigh, and named and numbered the fruit trees, apple and pear and vine and fig, which Laertes, forty years ago, had given to him for his own—then the old man doubted no longer, but embraced his son and thanked the Gods that he could die content.

Well, stranger, there's the story, as I heard it from my father's lips. Call it ended, if you will, and please yourself with the thought of Odysseus master of his own again, and happy in the possession of a loyal wife, a gallant son, and a fine estate.

But it's a true saying that what a man's born to be, that he is, and that he remains. Could Odysseus in the vigor of his manhood forsake for ever the call of the shadowy horizon beyond the sea, and live at ease? The course of his life after his home-coming no man knows for sure; but one thing I can tell you, and that's another dream among the many dreams he had in the Dark Land, the land of ghosts. It seemed to him as he lay on that tempestuous and inhospitable shore, that the ghost of Teiresias the prophet spoke to him, and told him—what was indeed the truth—that he would come safely home to Ithaca, though in sad plight and his companions drowned; but then it said that after many days he would once more set sail in a black ship, and traverse the illimitable sea until he came to an unknown country. There he would quit his ship and, taking an oar with him, journey inland until he reached a people who had never heard of ships or the sea, but asked in wonder what the thing was that he carried in his hand. Then he would plant the oar in the earth for a sign, and make his way homeward.

That indeed might be the end; but it seemed in his dream that there was one more word Teiresias spoke: that when Odysseus full of years came at last to die, it was from the sea he knew and loved so well, that death would rise to take him.

Did his dream come true? I don't know, stranger—and your guess is as good as mine.

I have talked long enough. The moon is as pale as ashes, and it will soon be dawn—then you'll see the island again, Odysseus' island, rocky Ithaca, flushed in the sunrise.

You have your journey before you, and it is time to sleep.

NOTE

My chief object in writing this book, apart from the pleasure people have always had in retelling old tales, was to whet the appetite of young readers so as to send them hunting for what could really and truly satisfy it. That, of course, is nothing other than the Odyssey *itself.*

The Odyssey, *which was written some twenty-eight centuries ago, has never been surpassed as a story of romantic adventure; and most boys and girls, who are not afraid of a big book, could read with delight any one of the excellent English translations which have been made of it. So after reading my* little *book, that is what I hope they will do.*